A HANDBOOK OF ANTHROPOMETRY

A HANDBOOK OF ANTHROPOMETRY

By

M. F. ASHLEY MONTAGU

With a Section on

The Measurement of Body Composition

By

JOSEF BROŽEK

CHARLES C THOMAS · PUBLISHER

Springfield · Illinois · U.S.A.

CHARLES C THOMAS · PUBLISHER
BANNERSTONE HOUSE
301-327 East Lawrence Avenue, Springfield, Illinois, U.S.A.

Published simultaneously in the British Commonwealth of Nations by
BLACKWELL SCIENTIFIC PUBLICATIONS, LTD., OXFORD, ENGLAND

Published simultaneously in Canada by
THE RYERSON PRESS, TORONTO

With THOMAS BOOKS careful attention is given to all details of
manufacturing and design. It is the Publisher's desire to present books
that are satisfactory as to their physical qualities and artistic possibilities
and appropriate for their particular use. THOMAS BOOKS will be true
to those laws of quality that assure a good name and good will.

Printed in the United States of America

To the Memory of

Aleš Hrdlička

and

J. Matiegka

PREFACE

THE PRESENT *Handbook of Anthropometry* is designed to be of use to all those who are in any way called upon to measure or to make observations upon the human body, whether it be the living body, the cadaver, or the skeleton. It is deliberately brief, and contains only those measurements and directions for anthroposcopic and other observations which are in most common use, and which, from long experience by several generations of anthropometrists, have been found to be most useful.

References to more exhaustive works on anthropometry will be found in the bibilography. It has been many years since a short handbook on anthropometry has been published, and since the present one is extracted and reprinted as a whole from the author's *An Introduction to Physical Anthropology* (Third edition, Springfield, Thomas, 1960), it should be stated that it is complete in itself and is in no way dependent upon the larger work. It is to be hoped that its separate publication will prove helpful to those who feel the need of such a work.

Professor Josef Brožek's section on the measurement of body composition will, it is to be hoped, stimulate many workers to undertake studies of the human body which have hitherto been omitted or neglected for want of the proper methods. The author wishes to express his thanks to Professor Brožek for his valuable contribution.

Princeton, N.J.   M. F. ASHLEY MONTAGU

CONTENTS

A HANDBOOK OF ANTHROPOMETRY

A PRACTICAL SYNOPSIS OF METHODS OF MEASUREMENT IN PHYSICAL ANTHROPOLOGY

THE MEASUREMENT OF MAN

THE FOLLOWING account is intended to give the reader a working knowledge of some of the methods of measurement most commonly used in physical anthropology. For a more complete account the reader should refer to the works listed on pages 127-129.

In view of the fact that no two persons are ever alike in all their measurable characters, that the latter tend to undergo change in varying degrees from birth to death, in health and in disease, and since persons living under different conditions, and members of different ethnic groups and the offspring of unions between them, frequently present interesting differences in bodily form and proportions, it is desirable to have some means of giving quantitative expression to the variations which such traits exhibit. *Anthropometry* constitutes that means. It is the technique of expressing quantitatively the form of the body. Anthropometry means the measurement of man, whether living or dead, and consists primarily in the measurement of the dimensions of the body.

While the methods of measurement used in physical anthropology are numerous, there are only two which are uniquely its contribution and which are peculiar to it, these are anthropometry and anthroposcopy. Other methods have been borrowed from anatomy, medicine, physiology, biochemistry, genetics, and statistics. In fact, physical anthropology makes use of every method which is capable of throwing light upon the significant likenesses and differences existing between individuals and groups of men.

Anthroposcopy is the visual observation and description of physical traits which do not easily lend themselves to exact measurement. For example, form and character and distribution of the hair, skin color, eye color, eye folds, form of lip, of nose, and the like.

3

Physiometry, the measurement of the physiological functions of the body, constitutes an important adjunct of anthropometry, the methods of which are mostly borrowed from physiology and serology.

Anthropometry is conveniently subdivided as follows:

Somatometry: The measurement of the body in the living and in the cadaver.
Cephalometry: Included in somatometry, the measurement of the head and face in the living and in the cadaver and from x-ray films.
Osteometry: The measurement of the skeleton and its parts.
Craniometry: Included in osteometry, the measurement of the skull.

The techniques of anthropometry are best acquired from an experienced worker in the field or laboratory. The attainment of accuracy in anthropometry requires a good deal of practice. A fundamental rule to bear in mind is that when a problem requiring the assistance of anthropometry is presented, all those parts of the body, and only those, should be measured which are capable of throwing some light upon that problem. If the form and dimensions of the lower jaw are the subject of principal interest, it is very unlikely that the length of the forearm will cast any additional light upon the problem. The dimensions of the head would seem more likely to be of assistance, and in any event constitute relevant information for an understanding of the lower jaw in its anatomico-physiological relationships, hence it were advisable to make relationally significant measurements of the head.

On the other hand if one is interested in relative growth, rates of growth may be discovered to exist for lower jaw and for upper and lower extremities which are similar. This, indeed, has been found to be the case.[1] In studies of growth few measurements can be irrelevant.

Before a measurement is projected it is useful to ask what purpose it is designed to serve. Every measurement constitutes an answer to a question, and as Cardinal Newman once remarked, any fool can ask meaningless questions. It is well to remember that the answer obtained to a question is largely determined by the structure of the question asked. Some questions are more meaningful than others. A measurement is a reply to the question: What is the extent, quantity or size of this dimension? The answer obtained does not necessarily express any fact other than that it has been determined according to the criteria or standards used. The purposes for which measurements are made may differ considerably. If, for example, the investigator is

---

[1] Shepherd, R. H., Sholl, and Vizoso, A.: The size relationship subsisting between body length, limbs and jaws in man. *J. Anat.,* 83:296-302, 1949.

interested in total height, his method of measurement will be very different from that followed by the investigator who is interested in discovering the rate of growth of the different components that enter into the conditioning of total height. The inquirer who is interested in objectifying genetic variation will attempt measurements that are refined enough to reflect the genetic conditions. These, of course, he will at best only approximate. The investigator interested in the growth of the head will make measurements that recognize the genetic and functional individuality of the many elements that go to make up the head, and he will therefore attempt to devise measurements that will individually serve to follow the changes in these elements as they grow and develop in relation to one another and to the head as a whole.

New methods based on sound principles may always be devised by an investigator to meet the demands of his particular problem. Measurements based on genuine functional biological relations are those most to be encouraged. The development of such biologically based measurements is to be preferred to the slavish repetition of those embalmed in anthropometric manuals, not excluding the present one.

Essential Historical Data

The history of the person measured should always be taken, since that history is to some extent part and parcel of the body being measured. Anthropometric findings should, so far as possible, always be evaluated in the light of the historical data. The following constitute the minimum historical data to be gathered:

Name	Religion
Sex	Occupation
Age, to the nearest birthday	Social status
Birthplace	Economic status
Ethnic group	Physical environment
Birth order, 1st, 2nd, etc.	First menstruation
Brothers	First conception
Sisters	Marital status
Mother's ethnic group	Children
Father's ethnic group	Illnesses

Instruments in Somatometry

The following instruments are those most commonly used in somatometric as well as in osteometric studies.

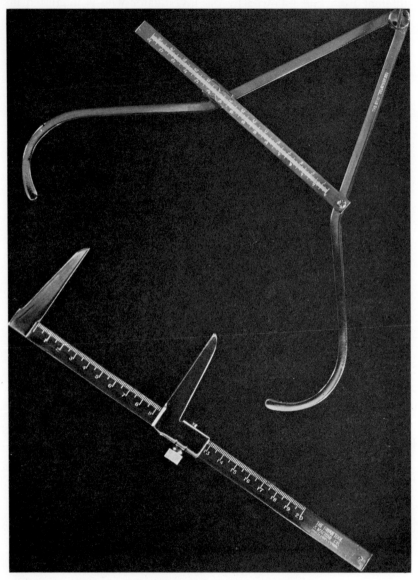

Figure 1. Sliding compass (below) and spreading calipers (above). (Photo Dr. Morris Steggerda and the Swan Tool and Machine Company, Hartford, Connecticut.)

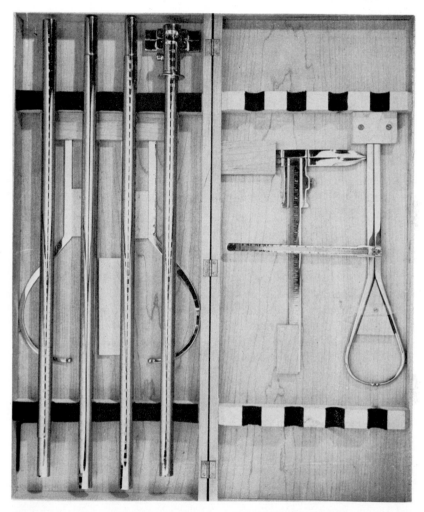

Figure 2. Case of basic anthropometric instruments. Anthropometer, sliding compass, and spreading calipers. (Courtesy of the manufacturers, Gilliland Instrument Co., Oakland, California.)

Weight Beam Scale.[2] To determine weight, preferably in grams.

Camera. Photography of subjects.

Measuring Tape. Graduated in millimeters, of good flexible steel.

Anthropometer.[3] For measuring height and various transverse diameters of the body, this convenient instrument generally consists of four hollow tubes which fit into one another to form a rigid rod of about two meters in length. Each tube is graduated in millimeters, one side reading from above and the other from below zero to two thousand millimeters. This instrument may be used for taking stature, sitting-height, and various other heights, as a caliper in taking transverse diameters, and as a pelvimeter.

Spreading Caliper.[4] For measuring such diameters of the head as the length and breadth of the head, bizygomatic diameter, etc.

Sliding Compass. For measuring shorter diameters such as those of the nose, ears, hand, etc.[5]

Head Spanner. For determining the height of the head.[6]

SOMATOMETRY

Measurement of the Dimensions of the Body

It is desirable to make most measurements with the subject in the standing position. To this rule measurements of the head and face, sitting-height, and a few others constitute the only exceptions.

Whenever possible all measurements should be made during the morning rather than the afternoon or evening, for the reason that individuals generally decrease in height from morning towards evening, and further because they tend to be more relaxed during the morning.

Where the body as a whole is being measured it is preferable that the subject be completely unclothed. When this is not possible the

---

[2] No. 66830, C. H. Stoelting & Company, Illinois, weighs up to 240 pounds, the beam is graduated in both pounds and grams. This balance scale is portable and therefore lends itself for use in field work. A remarkably light scale (total weight two pounds) is that developed by the late Dr. Morris Steggerda. This scale is capable of weighing a man of 325 pounds. It is obtainable from the Swan Tool and Manufacturing Machine Company, 30 Bartholomew Avenue, Hartford, Connecticut.

[3, 4, 5] May be inexpensively purchased from the Swan Tool and Manufacturing Machine Company, 30 Bartholomew Avenue, Hartford, Connecticut.

[6] This and all other anthropological instruments may be ordered from Siber Hegner & Co., Ltd., Talstrasse 14, Zurich, Switzerland. New York office: 183, Madison Avenue, New York 16, New York. Delivery: four to six weeks. U.S. duty: 45 per cent! Also Gilliland Instrument Co., Oakland, California.

investigator will have to make the best of the situation encountered. All measurements on the living should be made with a minimum of pressure by the instruments.

Landmarks (see Figures 3 and 4). In order that all measurements shall be comparable it is customary to take them from certain definite points, these are designated as landmarks. These landmarks will not be listed separately here but will be defined in connection with the measurements to be taken.

Measurements With Subject in Standing Position

Position of Subject. All measurements, unless otherwise indicated, should be made with the subject standing in the military position at attention, head erect, looking straight ahead, so that his visual axis is parallel to the surface of the floor. The latter is the best free approximation to the Frankfurt Plane (p. 15).

1. *Standing Height or Stature* (Anthropometer). The distance from the highest point of the top of the head in the mid-sagittal plane to the floor.

2. *Suprasternal Height* (Anthropometer). From the middle of the anterior-superior border of the manubrium sterni to the floor.

3. *Right Acromiale Height* (Anthropometer). From the most lateral projection of the lateral border of the acromion of the scapula to the floor.

4. *Right Radiale Height* (Anthropometer). From the highest point of the head of the radius (usually at the dimple of the elbow) to the floor.

5. *Right Stylion Height* (Anthropometer). From the distolateral end of the styloid process of the radius to the floor.

The *upper* and *lower arm dimensions* may be obtained by the subtraction of measurements 4 from 3 and 5 from 4, but are more accurately measured directly.

6. *Upper Arm Length* (Anthropometer). From acromiale to radiale when the arm is hanging down and the palm facing inward.

7. *Lower Arm Length* (Anthropometer). From radiale to stylion when the arm is hanging down and the palm facing inward.

8. *Total Arm Length* (Anthropometer). From acromiale to stylion when the arm is hanging down and the palm facing inward or by adding measurements 6 and 7.

9. *Total Upper Extremity Length* (Anthropometer). From acromiale to dactylion, *i.e.* the tip of the middle finger.

10. *Right Dactylon Height* (Anthropometer). From the middle of the tip of the middle finger when the fingers are removed from

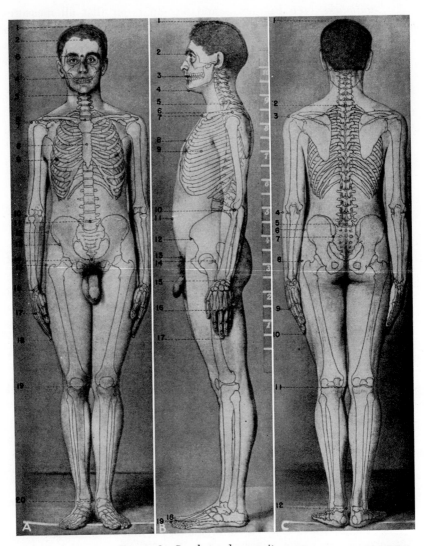

Figure 3. See legend opposite page.

contact with the thigh and are pointing perpendicularly downwards to the floor.

11. *Right Iliocristale Height* (Anthropometer). From the most laterally projecting point on the crest of the right ilium to the floor.

12. *Right Iliospinale Height* (Anthropometer). From the right anterior-superior iliac spine to the floor.

13. *Right Trochanterion Height* (Anthropometer). From the superior surface of the greater trochanter of the femur to the floor.

14. *Right Tibiale Height* (Anthropometer). From the superior surface of the medial condyle of the tibia to the floor.

15. *Right Sphyrion Height* (Anthropometer). From the inferior surface of the medial malleolus to the floor.

Transverse and Antero-Posterior Dimensions

16. *Span* (Anthropometer). The distance between the tips of the middle fingers of each hand when the arms are outstretched sidewards horizontally from the body. Measured from behind.

17. *Bi-Acromial Breadth* (Anthropometer used as sliding compass). The distance between the most lateral margins of the acromion processes of the scapula, the subject standing as he does normally.

18. *Chest Breadth or Transverse Diameter of the Thorax* (Anthropometer used as sliding compass. The transverse distance between the most lateral points on the chest. The mean of the measurements made at expiration and inspiration while the subject is breathing normally.

19. *Chest Depth or Antero-Posterior Diameter of the Thorax*

←

Figure 3. Landmarks of the body (after Martin).

Figure 3A. Landmarks on the frontal view. 1, vertex; 2, trichion; 3, nasion; 4, prosthion; 5, gnathion; 6, suprasternale; 7, akromion; 8, mesosternale; 9, thelion; 10, radiale; 11, omphalion 12, iliocristale; 13, iliospinale anterior; 14, symphysion; 15, trochanterion; 16, stylion; 17, phalangion; 18, daktylion; 19, tibiale; 20, sphyrion.

Figure 3B. Landmarks in the lateral view. 1, vertex; 2, nasion; 3, stomion; 4, gnathion; 5, cervicale; 6, akromion; 7, suprasternale; 8, mesosternale; 9, thelion; 10, radiale; 11, omphalion; 12, iliospinale anterior; 13, symphysion; 14, trochanterion; 15, stylion; 16, phalangion; 17, daktylion; 18, pternion; 19, akropodion.

Figure 3C. Landmarks in the posterior view. 1, vertex; 2, cervicale; 3, akromion; 4, radiale; 5, lumbale; 6, iliocristale; 7, iliospinale posterior; 8, trochanterion; 9, phalangion; 10, daktylion; 11, tibiale; 12, sphyrion.

(Large Spreading Caliper). At the level of the inferior angles of the scapulae. The mean of the measurements made at expiration and inspiration while the subject is breathing normally.

20. *Bi-Iliac or Pelvic Breadth* (Anthropometer used as a sliding compass). From iliocristale, the most lateral point on the crest of the ilium to iliocristale.

21. *Bi-Trochanteric or Hip Breadth* (Anthropometer used as a sliding compass). From trochanterion, the most lateral point on the great trochanter, to trochanterion.

Girths

22. *Axillary Chest Girth* (Tape). The tape applied well up in the axillary fossae. Mean reading of measurements during normal inspiration and expiration.

23. *Mesosternale Chest Girth* (Tape). At the level of the mesosternale. Mean of measurements during normal inspiration and expiration.

24. *Minimum Circumference of the Trunk-Waist Girth* (Tape). The minimum waist girth. Mean of measurements during normal inspiration and expiration.

25. *Maximum Gluteo-Pubic Circumference—Hip Girth* (Tape). The subject stands in the military position at attention. The tape is placed over the most prominent portion of the buttocks, is brought around the level of the greater trochanters to terminate anteriorly at the level determined by the buttocks and trochanters in the pubic region.

26. *Maximum Circumference of the Right Arm* (Tape). When the arm is hanging relaxed at the subject's side.

27. *Maximum Circumference of the Right Forearm* (Tape). Immediately distal to the elbow joint, with the whole extremity relaxed.

28. *Minimum Circumference of the Right Forearm—Girth of Wrist* (Tape). Slightly above the level of the styloid processes of the radius and ulna.

29. *Maximum Circumference of the Right Thigh* (Tape). Perpendicular to the long axis of the thigh, with the tape in the gluteal fold.

30. *Minimum Circumference of the Right Thigh* (Tape). Slightly proximal to the condyles of the femur.

31. *Maximum Circumference of the Right Leg—Girth of Calf* (Tape). The level of the maximum diameter above the floor should also be recorded.

32. *Minimum Circumference of the Right Leg—Girth of Ankle* (Tape). Slightly above the level of the malleoli.

Measurements With Subject in Sitting Position

Sitting Heights

A bench or box, high enough to keep the subject's feet away from the ground is placed against a wall, and the subject is instructed to take his seat in such a manner as to enable him to swing his legs freely over the front of the bench or box, while his scapular and sacral regions are resting vertically against the surface of the wall. In this position all measurements are taken from the specified landmark to the seat of the bench or box. The subject sits erectly with the head in the plane of the visual axis.

33. *Sitting Vertex Height* (Anthropometer). From the highest point, in the sagittal plane, of the head to the surface upon which the subject is seated.

34. *Sitting Suprasternale Height* (Anthropometer). From the middle of the anterior-superior border of the manubrium sterni to the floor.

By subtracting 34 from 33 the height of the head and neck is obtained.

Dimensions of the Hand and Foot

35. *Maximum Hand Length* (Sliding Compass). The hand is laid flat on a table. The distance from the mid-point of a line connecting the styloid processes of radius and ulna to the most anterior projection of the skin of the middle finger.

36. *Hand Breadth* (Sliding Compass). From the radial side of the second metacarpo-phalangeal junction to the ulnar side of the fifth metacarpo-phalangeal junction.

37. *Maximum Foot Length* (Spreading Calipers). From the most posteriorly projecting point on the heel (akropodion) to the tip of the most anteriorly projecting toe (pternion), when the subject is standing erect.

38. *Foot Breadth* (Anthropometer as Sliding Compass). From the medial margin of the head of the first metatarsal to the lateral margin of the head of the fifth metatarsal.

Dimensions of the Head

Measurements of the head are best made while the subject is comfortably seated in a chair. As for the rest of the body so in the case of the head, the measurements which the investigator will want to make upon the head will, for the most part, be determined by the nature of his problem. Below are given the measurements most generally made, but the investigator may devise others to suit the special requirements of his particular problem. Such new measurements, however, must have some morphological basis and should not begin and end, as it were, in thin air.

Before listing the measurements made to determine the various dimensions of the head it is necessary to define the landmarks from which such measurements are conventionally made. The position of these landmarks is shown in Figure 4.

Alare (al). The most lateral point on the wing of the nose.

Cheilion (ch). The most lateral point at the corner of the lips.

Ectocanthion (ex). Outer corner of the eye or palpebral opening.

Endocanthion (en). Inner corner of the eye or palpebral opening.

Euryon (eu). The most lateral point on the side of the head.

Frontotemporale (ft). The most medial (deepest) point on the incurvure of the temple, just above and lateral to the orbit (see Figure 4).

Glabella (g). The most prominent point, in the midsagittal plane, between the eyebrows.

Gnathion (gn). The lowest median point on the lower border of the mandible.

Gonion (go). The most lateral point upon the postero-inferior angle (formed by the ramus and the body) of the mandible.

Infradentale (id). The highest point on the gum between the mandibular central incisors.

Labrale inferius (li). The median point in the lower margin of the lower membranous lip.

Labrale superius (ls). The median point in the upper margin of the upper membranous lip.

Metopion (m). The median point of a line connecting the two frontal eminences.

Nasion (n). The point at which a horizontal tangential to the highest points on the superior palpebral sulci intersects the midsagittal plane (Figures 4A and 14). The subject should be looking straight ahead.

Ophryon (on). The median point of a line drawn tangent to the upper border of the eyebrows.

Opisthocranion (op). The point of most backward projection of the head, in the mid-plane.

Orbitale (or). The lowest point on the inferior orbital margin.

Otobasion inferius (obi). The lowest point at which the ear attaches to the side of the head.

Porion (po). The point 5.0 mm. above the middle of the external border of the roof of the cutaneous external auditory meatus.

Postaurale (pa). The most posterior point on the helix of the ear.

Preaurale (pra). The point at which a straight line drawn from the postaurale perpendicular to the long axis of the external ear meets the base of the external ear.

Pronasale (prn). The tip of the nose.

Prosthion (pr). The lowest point on the gum between the maxillary central incisors.

Stomion (sto). The central point in the oral fissure when the lips are closed.

Subaurale (sba). The lowest point on the inferior border of the ear lobule when the head is held in the Frankfurt Plane.

Subnasale (sn). The point at which the nasal septum, between the nostrils, merges with the upper cutaneous lip in the mid-sagittal plane.

Superaurale (sa). The highest point on the superior border of the helix.

The Frankfurt Plane or Horizontal (F.H.). The plane determined by the lowest points on the infra-orbital margins (the *orbitalia*, "or" in Figure 4B) and the tragion or tragial notch of the ear ("t" in Figure 4A). This corresponds almost exactly to the plane of the visual axis, which obtains when the individual is looking straight ahead of him.

Tragion (t). The notch immediately above the tragus of the ear.

Trichion (tr). The mid-point at the hairline on the forehead.

Tuberculare (tu). Darwin's point on the ear; the tubercle on the upper portion of the helix.

Vertex (v). The highest point of the head, in the mid-sagittal plane, when the head is held erectly or in the Frankfurt Plane.

Zygion (z). The lateralmost point on the zygomatic arch.

CEPHALOMETRY

Measurements of the Head

Maximum Head Length (Spreading Caliper). The distance between the glabella and the farthest projecting point in the mid-sagittal plane, on the back of the head (occiput). The latter point is termed the opisthocranion.

Maximum Head Breadth (Spreading Caliper). The greatest transverse diameter of the head. This is usually found at a point over each parietal bone (each point is termed the euryon).

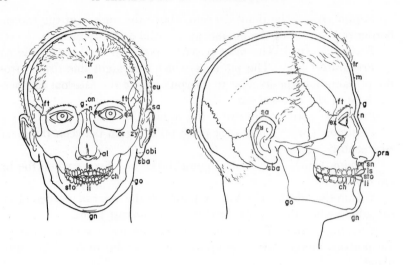

Figure 4A   Figure 4B

Figure 4. A. Landmarks in the frontal view of the head. B. Landmarks in the lateral view of the head. al, alare; ch, chelion; ex, ectocanthion; en, endocanthion; eu, euryon; ft, frontotemporale; g, glabella; gn, gnathion; go, gonion; li, labrale inferius; ls, labrale superius; m, metopion; n, nasion; on, ophryon; op, opisthocranion; or, orbitale; obi, otobasion inferius; prn, pronasale; pr, prosthion; sba, subaurale; sn, subnasale; sa, superaurale; t, tragion; tr, trichion; tu, tuberculare; zy, zygion. (From Martin, *Lehrbuch der Anthropologie,* 1928. Courtesy, Gustav Fischer, Jena.)

Head Height (Todd's Head-Spanner). The fiber-tipped movable horizontal rods are inserted into the ear-holes so that they touch the roof of the latter, the rods are then secured by screws. The orbital arm is then placed at the level of the most inferior point on the infra-orbital margin and kept there. As long as this position is maintained the head is in the Frankfurt Plane in relation to the measuring ruler. The latter is then released to the level of the top of the head, and the measurement read off. Eight mm. may be deducted from this measurement to allow for the thickness of the skin and subjacent tissues, should the height of the skull be desired. Five millimeters should then also be deducted to allow for the thickness of the tissues forming the roof of the ear-hole.

Minimum Frontal Breadth (Spreading Caliper). The shortest distance between the origins of the zygomatic processes of the frontal bones (the fronta-temporales, "ft" in Figures 4A and 4B).

Bizygomatic Breadth (Spreading Caliper). The distance between the most laterally situated points on the zygomatic arches (the zygia, "zy" in Figure 4B).

Bigonial Breadth (Spreading Caliper). The distance between the gonial points.

Physiognomic Facial Length (Sliding Compass). From trichion to gnathion.

Morphological Facial Height (Sliding Compass). From nasion to gnathion.

Total Jaw Height (Sliding Compass). From subnasale to gnathion. The jaws must be normally closed without undue pressure.

Inter-Canthic Diameter (Sliding Compass). From the medial point of the junction of the upper and lower eyelids ("en" in Figure 4A) of one side to the other.

Extra-Canthic Diameter (Sliding Compass). From the lateral point of the junction of the upper and lower eyelids ("ex" in Figure 4A) of the one side to the other.

Nasal Length (Sliding Compass). From nasion to subnasale.

Maximum Physiognomic Nasal Breadth (Sliding Compass). The maximum transverse distance between the most laterally situated points on the wings of the nose (the alare, "al" in Figure 4A).

Maximum Breadth of the Mouth (Sliding Compass). The maximum breadth of the mouth when the face is in a relaxed condition (from "ch" to "ch" in Figure 4A).

Physiognomic Ear Height (Sliding Compass). The distance between the superaurale and the subaurale ("sa" and "sba" in Figure 4B).

Physiognomic Ear Breadth (Sliding Compass). The distance between the preaurale and the postaurale ("pra" and "pa" in Figure 4B).

Girths

39. *Maximum Circumference of the Head* (Tape). From the smooth area between eyebrows (glabella) around the maximum projection of the occiput (opisthocranion) to the glabella.

40. *Circumference of Neck* (Tape). At the level of the most prominent portion of the thyroid cartilage.

Indices

An index, as used in anthropometry, is the ratio of one measurement to another expressed as a percentage of the larger one. Thus, if it is desired to determine the proportional relation of the breadth of the head to its length, the length is equated to the value of 100, and the breadth is then expressed as a ratio of 100. This yields the cephalic index, in which breadth is to length as x is to 100, the value of x being found by multiplying the actual value of the breadth by 100 and dividing by the actual length. Thus:

$$\frac{\text{Breadth} \times 100}{\text{Length}} = \text{Cephalic Index (x).}$$

By means of indices obtained in this way, it is possible to convey an exact idea of the proportion which one measurement bears to another, and thus something of the form of the structures concerned, in a single numerical expression. For example, a cephalic index of 75 per cent means that the breadth of the head is to its length as 75 is to 100; which clearly means that the breadth of the head is equal to three-fourths of its length or is 75 per cent of its length. An index greater than 75 would mean that the head was so much broader in relation to its length, and an index below 75 would mean the opposite. Thus, an index of 100 would mean that the head was as broad as it is long, and an index of 50 that the breadth of the head was exactly equal to half its length.

The number of indices which have been devised are almost countless. A good general rule to follow is to use or devise only such indices as are absolutely necessary to the prosecution, and the presentation of the results, of an investigation.

In comparing any two measurements it is sometimes convenient to refer them to some definite standard, preferably one which is not too variable. Total stature and sitting height are as near as we can get to such standards, and any bodily measurement may be expressed as an index with reference to total height or sitting height, thus:

$$\frac{\text{any bodily measurement} \times 100}{\text{total height or stature}} = \text{stature index of measurement used}$$

$$\frac{\text{any bodily measurement} \times 100}{\text{sitting height}} = \text{sitting height index of measurement used}$$

The following represent some of the anthropometric indices most commonly used:

$$\text{Cephalic index} = \frac{\text{Maximum Head Breadth} \times 100}{\text{Maximum Head Length}}$$

Dolichocephalic	$\times - 75.9$
Mesocephalic	$76.0 - 80.9$
Brachycephalic	$81.0 - 85.4$
Hyperbrachycephalic	$85.5 - \times$

$$\text{Brachial Index} = \frac{\text{Length of Forearm} \times 100}{\text{Length of Upper Arm}}$$

$$\text{Forearm-Hand Index} = \frac{\text{Hand Length} \times 100}{\text{Length of Forearm}}$$

$$\text{Hand Index} = \frac{\text{Hand Breadth} \times 100}{\text{Hand Length}}$$

$$\text{Tibio-Femoral Index} = \frac{\text{Length of Lower Leg} \times 100}{\text{Length of Thigh}}$$

$$\text{Lower Leg-Foot Index} = \frac{\text{Length of Foot} \times 100}{\text{Length of Lower Leg}}$$

$$\text{Intermembral Index} = \frac{\text{Length of Entire Arm} \times 100}{\text{Length of Entire Leg}}$$

$$\text{Femero-Humeral Index} = \frac{\text{Length of Upper Arm} \times 100}{\text{Length of Thigh}}$$

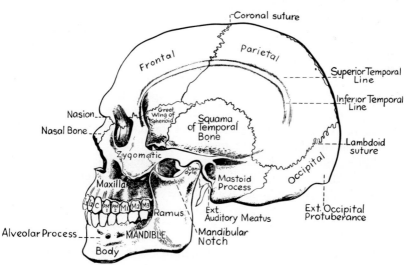

Figure 5. The Human skull.

Tibio-Radial Index $= \dfrac{\textbf{Length of Forearm} \times 100}{\textbf{Length of Lower Leg}}$

Trunk Index $= \dfrac{\textbf{Biacromial Breadth} \times 100}{\textbf{Sitting Suprasternale Height}}$

There are many more indices than these, but it is unnecessary to deal with them here. Additional lists of indices will be found in the works on anthropometry cited in the bibliography.

A large number of constitutional indices have been devised, but not one of these has yet proved satisfactory, for the reason that constitution is far too complex a thing to be expressible in terms of a single index.[7]

CRANIAL CAPACITY IN THE LIVING

This may be computed by the Lee-Pearson formula, as follows: For *males*, .000337 (cephalic length — 11) $\times$ (cephalic breadth — 11) $\times$ (ear head-height — 11) + 406.01; for *females*, .0004 (cephalic length — 11) $\times$ (cephalic breadth — 11) $\times$ (ear head-height — 11) + 206.60.

ANTHROPOSCOPIC OBSERVATIONS

In making visual observations on the subject the investigator must strive to attain the greatest precision, to eliminate the element of subjective judgment, and to obtain as objective a record as possible. The ideal at which to aim is the attainment of standards of accuracy which are as nearly quantitatively expressible as possible. Hence, methods contributing towards this end are, in all instances, to be preferred. The development of such methods is an urgent desideratum. Many anthroposcopic methods at present in use are hopelessly unreliable. Only a few of those available methods can be dealt with here which are capable of yielding relatively sound and comparable observations.

All observations should be made in good light.

Abbreviations which have been used in recording some observations are: abs = absent, undeveloped, none; sl. = slight, very small; sm. = small, submedium, few; + = average, medium, several; + + = above average, large, pronounced, many; + + + = great, very many, extraordinary development; ? = not observable.

1. *Somatotype.* Made from photographs taken in the standard positions described hereunder in direction 18, (pp. 26-27).

---

[7] For a list of constitutional indices see Tucker, W.B. and Lessa, W. A.: Man: a constitutional investigation. *Quart. Rev. Biol.*, 15:413-414, 1940.

2. *General Sex Facies or Appearance* (after establishment of puberty).

Whether the mature subject appears to deviate from normalcy; whether he is hypogonadal or gynandromorphic, infantile or juvenile, masculine or feminine (in the opposite sex), adult or senile. By "hypogonadal" is to be understood inadequate development of the secondary sexual characters. By "gynandromorphy" the degree or prominence of the secondary sexual characters of the one sex present in a member of the opposite sex. Since many groups differ from American North European white standards, the observer should take great care in arriving at his standard of the norm in such groups.

3. *Skin Color.* There is no rule as to where skin color should be taken.

The inner surface of the upper arm has been frequently used on the assumption that it is a region not too much exposed to sunlight. Whatever region is used should be used constantly in the series under investigation. Skin color should be determined by the use of some fast and easily reduplicable color standard. The best available color standards are obtainable from the non-profit Munsell Color Company (of which Mrs. B. R. Bellamy is manager), 10 East Franklin Street, Baltimore 2, Maryland. It will be found useful to cut a small square out of a piece of cardboard, and hold this over the desired area on the subject for comparison with the color squares on the Munsell charts. This eliminates the distraction of adjoining areas of skin color and speeds accurate matching of colors.

Record presence and position of any variably pigmented areas, including the so-called "blue-spot" (miscalled "Mongoloid spot") in sacral region of infants.

4. *Hair Color.* Scalp, face, and body hair, eyebrows, mustache, beard, chest, abdomen, pubes, and extremities, to be observed and recorded separately. Use Munsell color standards. Collect samples of hair and record area from which taken.

5. *Hair Form.* Usually but quite inadequately described as: Straight, low wave, medium wave, deep wave, curly, frizzly or kinky, and coiled or spiral tufts (pepper corn).

Dr. Stanley Garn has kindly supplied the following comments on hair form:

Human head hair exists in a complete range of forms, with hair that is nearly straight and hair that curls into tight spirals representing the extremes of the human distribution.

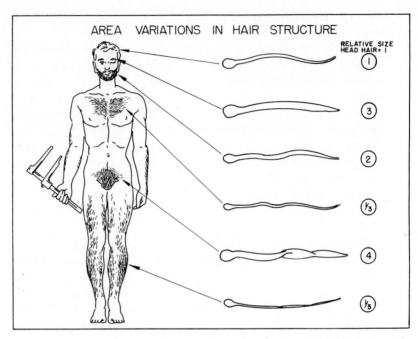

Figure 6. Area variations in structure and relative size of hair in male. (Courtesy, Dr. S. M. Garn.)

Figure 7. Skin folds over the upper eyelid in man. →The right eye is shown with the root of the nose, nasion, toward the middle of the page. a, complete Mongoloid fold, b, internal epicanthic fold, c, no fold, d, external epicanthic fold, e, median fold. a′, mid-sagittal section showing the relation of the skin fold to the upper eyelid in the Mongoloid, and c′ in the non-Mongoloid. (Modified after Hooton, *Up From the Ape*, 1946. Courtesy, The Macmillan Co.)

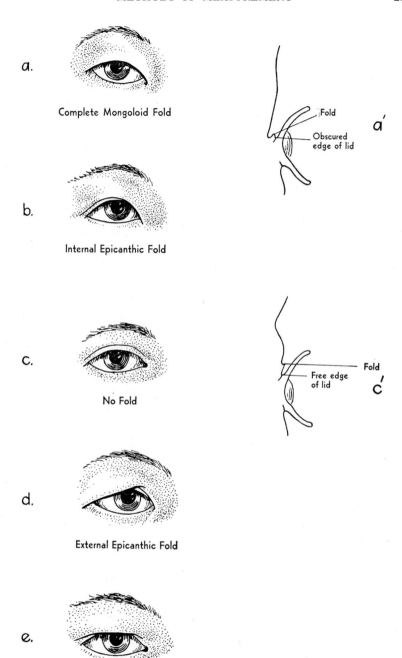

a.

Complete Mongoloid Fold

Fold

Obscured
edge of lid

a'

b.

Internal Epicanthic Fold

c.

No Fold

Fold

Free edge
of lid

c'

d.

External Epicanthic Fold

e.

Figure 7. See legend opposite page.

Actually, no human hair is completely straight, but if the radius of curvature is larger than that of the head, it appears straight when short, and hangs straight by its own weight if long. When the curvature is in one direction, the hair forms ringlets or helices. With reversing or alternating curvature the hair is "wavy," whereas very small radii of curvature, becoming progressively slightly larger, are characteristic of the spiral-tuft type. The best description of hair form is therefore not verbal, but mathematical, thus avoiding a needless series of descriptive categories.

Clearly, variations in the form of the hair are due to localized growth gradients in the follicle, with obvious synchronia among adjacent hair follicles. The form of hair that a given follicle will produce is apparently determined genetically, occasionally by a single pair of genes, but more commonly by the cumulative action of many genes. Hormonal influences also affect hair curvature, sometimes by controlling the rate of hair growth, or hair thickness.

By analogy with the propagation of light waves, one can view variations in hair form as due to oscillations within the follicle during growth. The more rapid the oscillations, the shorter is the wave-length, and, if the rotatory movement is continuous, helices and spirals are superimposed upon the growing hairs. With synchronous follicular activity, hairs in a given region, comprising a lock, have similar degrees of curvature. This is especially evident in the fur of the Karakul lamb, and in poodles, and people with helical and spiral-locks.

Where hair-straightening or hair curling is not practiced, measurements of the wavelength (distance between peaks), amplitude, radius of curvature, furnish useful genetically-meaningful data for mathematical analysis.

6. *Hair Quantity.* Number of hairs in a square centimeter of scalp; whether thick, medium, thinning, thin; degree and pattern of baldness.
7. *Eye Color.* With the subject in good light and facing a white surface the iris is matched with Munsell color samples. Record raying, zoning, and spotting of iris.
8. *Supraorbital Ridges.* Absent, slight, medium, and pronounced.
9. *Ear Form.* Degree of rolling of helix; whether lobe of ear is free or attached; Darwin's point; size; shape.

10. *Eyefolds.* The arrangements of the skin over the upper eyelids and canthi.

Described and defined as follows (see Figure 7):

    i. *Complete Mongoloid Fold:* The skin above the upper eyelid is loose and hangs down over the free margin of the eyelid.

    ii. *Internal Epicanthic Fold:* The skin hangs over the inner canthus alone.

    iii. *External Epicanthic Fold:* The skin hangs over the external canthus alone.

    iv. *No Fold:* The skin forms a gentle arch above the upper eyelid.

    v. *Median Fold:* The skin hangs down over the middle part of the margin of the upper eyelid and leaves both canthi exposed.

    vi. *Pseudo-Mongoloid Fold:* Usually present in babies but disappears within a year or two with growth; occurs often as an age change in older people, simulating the appearance of the complete Mongoloid fold.

11. *Nose Form.*

    i. *Nasal Profile:* Concave, straight, convex, concavo-convex.

    ii. *Nasal Root:* Flat, recessed, medium, prominent.

    iii. *Nasal Tip:* Narrow, medium, thick, bulbous.

12. *Nostrils.* Broad, oval, round. Angle in relation to mid-sagittal plane.

13. *Lips.*

    i. *Membranous:* Thin, medium, thick, very thick; degree of eversion.

    ii. *Integumental:* Thickness.

14. *Dentition.* A dental form showing the occlusal surfaces of the teeth of the upper and lower jaws should be used, and all observations marked, whenever possible, directly upon the teeth referred to. The S. S. White Dental Manufacturing Company supplies useful record cards for this purpose. A dental mirror will be found useful. The following details should be noted:

    i. *Occlusion or Bite:* Estimated horizontal distance between upper and lower incisors. Recorded as + when upper teeth are in advance of the lower; as — when lower teeth are in advance of the upper.

    ii. Level above gum of erupting teeth, in millimeters.

   iii. Shovel-shaped incisors.

   iv. Supernumerary teeth.

    v. Congenitally missing teeth.

   vi. Unerupted teeth.

  vii. Crowding.

 viii. Rotation.

   ix. Accessory cusps or tubercles.

    x. Wear of occlusal surfaces.

   xi. Teeth lost by extraction or otherwise.

  xii. Caries.

 xiii. Fissural patterns of occlusal surfaces of mandibular three molars, Y5, +5, Y4, or +4.

15. *Mandibular Torus.* Bony thickening, inner sides of mandible.
16. *Palatal Form.* Narrow, intermediate, broad; low, medium, high. Whether torus palatinus (a piling up of bone along the course of the palatine intermaxillary suture which may be felt and often seen at the median raphe in the living) is present.
17. *Chin Form.* Pointed, rounded, square; receding, vertical, slight, medium, marked protrusion. The observer must define his standards and consistently adhere to them.
18. *Standard Photographs.* The aim should be to obtain photographs which give as complete a view of the nude body as possible and all its outlines. This is particularly necessary for somatotyping. Full length views of the front, back, and left side are desirable. Front view and left profile photographs of the head may be taken as supplementary, or when full views in the nude are not possible. The subject should always be placed at a constant distance from the lens of the camera, the background should always be as nearly uniform as possible, and floor, wall or ground and background so arranged that they merge in the photograph, and preferably appear *white.* For purposes of standard reproduction any background may be air-brushed white. Use panchromatic film. Women should pile the hair on top of the head in a hair net, in order not to obscure the outlines of the neck and shoulders.

Frontal View

    i. Subject in normal standing position breathing normally, with lower extremities just sufficiently separated so that the inner aspects of the thighs do not touch.

ii. Eyes looking straight ahead.
iii. Arms, hands, and fingers straight. Lock olecranon process.
iv. Hands five inches out from thighs.
v. Right and left hands palm facing thigh.

Left Profile

i. Arms, hands, and fingers straight. Held flat against the body in center of body outline, so that neither elbow nor hand break the outline behind or in front.
ii. Knees and legs perfectly in line. Do not lock.
iii. Face in perfect profile, subject looking straight ahead.

Back View

i. As front. If lighting is oblique arms should be carried forward to prevent shadow on flanks.[8]

[8] For the most recent recommendations for the standardization of techniques in posing the subject see Dupertuis, C. W. and Tanner, J. M.: The pose of the subject for photogrammetric anthropometry, with especial reference to somatotyping. *Am. J. Phys. Anthropol.*, n.s. 8:27-47, 1950.

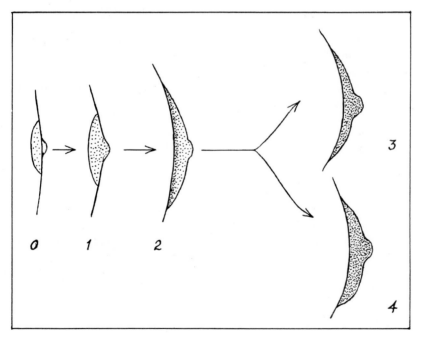

Figure 8. Four stages in areolar development of the white female. (Modified after Garn and Shamir.)

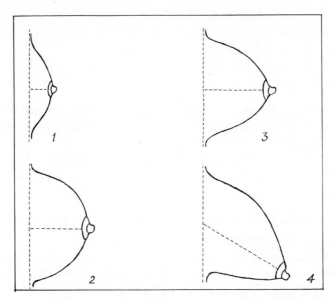

Figure 9. Schematic representation of breast shapes. 1. Bowl-shaped. 2. Hemispherical. 3. Conical. 4. Elongated.

19. *Papillae, Areolae, Breasts.* The elements of the breasts, papillae, areolae, and the fatty main body of the breasts should be carefully distinguished. Record all anomalies and asymmetries, and supernumerary elements.

Papillae: Flat, infantile, everted, and their size indicated.
Areolae: 0 Infantile, small, flat, lightly pigmented.
   1 Early-maturing, pigmentation still developing, areolae separately elevated from body of breast, papilla buried.
   2 Later-maturing, there is a marked ring of pigmentation at the periphery, papilla still buried.
   3 Mature Areolae no longer separately elevated, papilla everted.
   4 Mature Areolae separately elevated, papilla everted.
Breast Form:
   1. Bowl-shaped, in which the anterior projection is less than the radius of the circumference.
   2. Hemispherical, in which the anterior projection is equal to the radius of the circumference.

3. Conical, in which the anterior projection is greater than the radius.
4. Dependent, with the papillae pointing downwards.

20. *Lumbar Curvature.* Slight, moderate, marked.
21. *Buttocks.* Flat, medium, prominent, steatopygious.
22. *External genitalia.* In the male penis may be measured from pubis to external os, in flaccid condition. In female, size of labia may be recorded.
23. *Hands and Feet.* Note any webbing of fingers or toes, or any other anomalies. Note shape of nails, as long-narrow, short-broad, etc. The relative projection of fingers and toes in relation to each of their fellows is expressible in the *digital formula*. In the hand one begins counting with the thumb as 1, the index-finger as 2, the middle finger as 3, the ring-finger as 4, and the little finger as 5. The most projecting finger is written first. For example, if the middle finger projects furthest, and the ring-finger further than the index-finger, and the index-finger further than the little finger, and the little finger further than the thumb, one writes the digital formula thus: 3>4>2>5>1. The same procedure is followed for the toes, counting the big toe as 1 and the little toe as 5. Supernumerary digits or toes and all other possible variations and anomalies may be recorded.

Finger, Palm, Toe, and Sole Prints

The skin on the palmar and plantar surfaces of the human hand and foot differs in character from that covering other parts of the body. The palmar and plantar skin is corrugated into continuous ridges and lacks both hairs and sebaceous (oil) glands. Sweat glands are, however, numerous. These corrugated ridges are known as friction ridges and are present in all primates.[9] These ridges are obviously of great assistance in handling and grasping since they help to counteract slipping. Since from the time of their formation in the early fetus to the final disintegration of the skin after death the patterns which these ridges present remain unaltered [10] they are of use not only for the purpose of identification, in recognizing types of twins, but also in

---

[9] For a comprehensive study see Midlo, C. and Cummins, H.: Palmar and Plantar Dermatoglyphics in Primates. *American Anatomical Memoirs,* No. 20, Philadelphia, Wistar Inst., 1942.

[10] The ridges on the terminal digits may be so worn down as to be invisible. This is often the case in stenographers. In shoeless people (who habitually wear no shoes) the plantar and toe ridges may be similarly worn down.

studies of heredity, raciation, sex differences, growth, bodily symmetry, and comparative primatology. *Dermatoglyphics (derma,* skin—*glyphe,* carve) is the name given to the study of the ridge patternings of the skin of the fingers, palms, toes, and soles.

The materials necessary for making finger and palm prints, toe and sole prints are the following: A plate of lucite or bakelite 8″ x 10″ and ¼″ thick, a tube of printer's ink, a rubber roller, and a good grade of white, *not* highly sized, paper or the standard cards customarily in use measuring 8″ x 8″ for finger prints.

An even film of ink is spread on the lucite or bakelite base, and each finger is then rolled firmly from the inner to the outer edge on the film, the same operation then being repeated upon the paper or cards.

A solvent should be available with which to clean fingers. Fingers for printing should be perfectly clean and dry. After the prints have been made the solvent may be used to remove the ink from the fingers.

In palm printing the inked roller is passed several times over the whole area to be printed from the base of the fingers where they join the palm to the flexion creases on the wrist. The ulnar or little finger side of the subject's palm is then laid against the paper and the hand rolled palm downward to the radial or thumb side. Appreciable pressure must be applied to the back of the hand and over the knuckles in order to obtain satisfactory impressions of the central portions of the palms and bases of the fingers. It is essential to print each tri-radius (triangular group of consolidated ridges) at the base of each finger, as well as the carpal tri-radius located at the base of the thumb.

The sole is inked and printed in the same way as the palm. Each toe is printed separately. Persons suffering from athlete's foot should not be printed even if their friction ridges are visible.

PHYSIOMETRIC OBSERVATIONS

The measurement of the physiological functions of the body will include functions which are sensibly influenced by environmental factors like pulse and even color vision, and some that are not, such as the ability to taste certain substances which is a genetically conditioned trait. A distinction between modifiable physiological functions and genetically conditioned functional traits will not be made here, though the distinction can, of course, and should for certain purposes, be made.

Ten basic observations are here listed which can be made with a reasonable degree of expedition and considerable accuracy.

The subject should always be examined alone. The presence of other persons is distracting, and the desire to imitate or look for clues in the behavior of others confusing. Among non-literate peoples special precautions and cross-checking must be instituted in order to make quite certain the instructions have been understood and the desire of the subject to please has not been too overwhelming.

1. *Physical Fitness or Step Test.* Take pulse with stop-watch. Write down the mean of four one-minute observations. The subject is then asked to step rapidly on and off a 12 inch step or platform for one minute. The exact pace is set with a metronome. Take pulse immediately after subject has completed this operation and determine how long the pulse takes to return to normal.

2. *Dynamometric Strength.* Use a physician's dynamometer with light attached. The mean of the maximum of three squeezes with the hand customarily used for squeezing.

3. *Resistance to Ulta-Violet Ray Burning.* Ethnic variations in sensitivity to skin burning as exhibited in erythema or reddening of the skin due to ultra-violet radiation is something concerning which we know very little. In view of the possibility of selective differences in the frequency of this trait as between different ethnic groups it would be of considerable interest to know whether or not such differences exist. An apparatus suitable for this purpose has been successfully used by Dr. George Levene of Massachusetts Memorial Hospitals, Boston. This consists of a small ultra-violet generator which measures 3 x 6 x 18 inches and weighs a little over seven pounds. There is a one inch square window which is applied to the surface of the skin for a predetermined period of time. The instrument is extremely critical in its radiation, with an intensity exposure of 2,537 angstrom units. The constancy of characteristic tube radiation is controlled by measureing the output from time to time with a special ultra-violet photometer. When the type of radiation varies the lamp is replaced. The degree of erythema or reddening can be measured either by determining the temperature difference between the area of erythema and non-exposed skin by means of a sensitive thermocouple, or by color comparison using the standard Munsell color charts.

This apparatus was designed by Mr. Ronald J. McKenzie of Sylvania Electric Products, Inc., 126 Washington Street, Salem, Massachusetts, who will be glad to answer inquiries concerning it.

For use in the field an electric current supply is, of course, necessary.

4. *Handedness.* Whether subject habitually uses one hand in preference to the other, or is ambidextrous.

TABLE I

CONCENTRATIONS OF P.T.C. SOLUTIONS

Solution No.	P.T.C. Mgm. per Liter
1	1300.00
2	650.00
3	325.00
4	162.00
5	81.25
6	40.63
7	20.31
8	10.16
9	5.08
10	2.54
11	1.27
12	0.63
13	0.32
14	0.16

5. *Ability to Taste PTC (Phenyl-Thio-Carbamide).* The best method of testing ability to taste phenyl-thio-carbamide at various graded standard measurable concentrations is that developed by Harris and Kalmus. A solution containing 0.13% of phenyl-thio-carbamide (or phenylthiourea) is made up with boiled tap water, and serial dilutions made up as in Table I.

(1) Starting from the higher dilutions and working down, the subject is given a few c.c. in a glass till he says he perceives a definite taste. This gives an approximate value for his threshold.

(2) The subject is now presented with eight glasses four of which contain a few c.c. of water and four contain a few c.c. of the solution determined in stage (1). The glasses are arranged at random. The subject is told that four of them contain the substance and four contain water, and he is asked to taste them all and to separate them into the two groups of four. The quantity of fluid is not limited, and glasses are refilled during the test if desired. If the two groups of four are correctly separated the test is repeated with the next lower concentration and so on, until the subject can no longer discriminate correctly The lowest concentration at which a completely correct answer is given is taken as the threshold. If, on the other hand, the subject is unable to separate the two groups accurately, the test is repeated in the same manner with increasing concentrations till a concentration is reached when a completely correct answer is given. Since there are both sexual and age differences in the threshold ability to taste PTC, age and sex should be carefully recorded for each subject.

In the field it may not be possible to use the above method. Under such conditions the following is a useful procedure:

A slip of paper impregnated with phenyl-thio-carbamide is given to the subject and he is asked to place it upon the back of the tongue. He is then asked whether he tastes anything. If the subject is a taster he will reply in terms indicating that he tastes something bitter. If he is a non-taster he will generally indicate that he tastes nothing. Record those who are in doubt as to whether they taste anything with a question mark. In order to test the genuineness of replies each subject should be given several tests with blank strips among those offered. Some individuals detect the bitter taste almost immediately. Others have to chew the paper for some time before the taste becomes detectable to them. It is necessary to make certain that the paper used before impregnation with PTC is itself entirely free of chemicals that yield a bitter taste. Careful records should be kept to distinguish early from late tasters, for there are apparently two dominant alleles involved. A stop-watch is helpful here.

6. *Ability to Smell Hydrocyanic Acid.* ☠ THIS HIGHLY POISONOUS SUBSTANCE, potassium cyanide, in solution, cannot be smelled by a certain proportion of individuals. It is vitally important in using this test material to take every precaution against the possibility of its being erroneously taken by mouth, for one sip is likely to be fatal. Antidotes: Inhalation amyl nitrite in handkerchief held lightly over nose, meanwhile cause vomiting by giving one pint of 1 per cent sodiumthiosulfate or soapy water or mustard water by mouth. Do not give anything by mouth to unconscious subject.

7. *Ability to Roll Sides of Tongue Upward When Mouth is Open.* If the investigator is able to perform this act he should show the subject what is required. If he is unable to do so he should stick out his tongue and with his fingers press against the edges of the tongue thus rolling the sides upwards. The literate subject will not generally require any demonstration. The ability to roll the tongue into a U-shape when the mouth is open is due to a dominant gene *R*.

8. *Ability to Turn One Side of the Tongue Up, With the Mouth Open.* The subject is asked to rotate the tongue so that the left side is upward and the right remains either stationary or is lowered, and vice versa. Sides to be recorded for ability and nonability.

9. *Color Blindness.* Best tested with the *Dvorine Color Discrimination Screening Test,* obtainable from Israel Dvorine, 2328 Eutaw Place, Baltimore 17, Maryland. Tests A and B should be used.

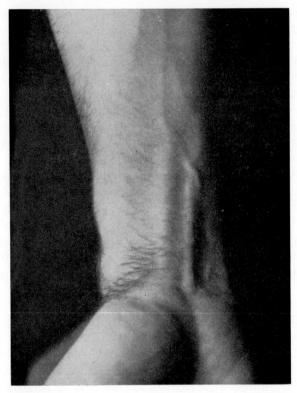

Figure 10. The palmaris longus muscle. The prominent tendon toward outer margin of this page is the palmaris longus. The right forearm is shown.

10. *Pigmentation of Iris.* A dominant gene *P* is responsible for the pigment at the front layer of the iris. The momozygous recessive genes *pp* are responsible for there being pigment particles present for the most part only in the posterior layer of the iris, thus yielding "blue" eyes. The Munsell Color Chart should be used in determining eye color (see p. 21).

11. *Interlocking Fingers and Thumb.* When the fingers are locked some individuals will invariably place the left thumb over the right thumb. This is due to a dominant gene *F*. Placing the right thumb over the left is due to a recessive gene *f*. Simply ask the individual to interlock his fingers.

12. *Palmaris Longus Muscle.* The central tendon of the forearm at the wrist which is normally visible and can be well defined when the subject's fingers are flexed upon the wrist. Three tendons are

generally visible in this region, one on the thumb side of the wrist (flexor carpi radialis) and one on the little finger side (flexor carpi ulnaris). The tendon of the palmaris longus muscle is situated between them. It is the most central tendon of the wrist. Record presence or absence. Presence is due to a pair of recessive genes *ll*, absence to a dominant gene *L*. Record condition in both wrists.

13. *Serological Traits.* A knowledge of the gene frequency distribution of the A-B-O blood groups, the blood types M, N, MN, and MNSs, and the Rh types in man is of considerable value in the study of human relationships.

If blood testing cannot conveniently be done the investigator should make complete arrangements with the scientific worker or workers within easiest reach to do the testing. Such complete arrangements will, of course, include the manner of preservation, sealing, and sending of blood samples.

If it is desired to send blood any distance or to keep it for more than a day, about 5 c.c. of blood should be taken with a sterile syringe under aseptic conditions, placed in a sterile tube with sterile stopper and allowed to clot. A suitable cell suspension can be made from this. If the blood is going to be tested promptly a sample may be taken directly into 0.9% sodium chloride solution by pricking the lobe of the ear or a finger, or in the case of infants the big toe, with a spring blood lancet. The skin and the blade of the lancet should be cleaned with alcohol or acetone, waiting for the disinfectant to evaporate before taking the blood.

Preservatives do not help a great deal. However, red cells remain agglutinable (for A, B, M, and N) for some weeks if preserved in Rous-Turner solution (3.8% sodium citrate solution 2 parts, 5.4% glucose solution 5 parts) or preferably in the ACD (citric acidcitrate-dextrose) mixture used in blood banks.

The A-B-O blood groups can often be determined from dried blood stains, mummified tissues, and even from skeletal remains of the recent period if they are in a suitable state of preservation.

Blood Typing Technique

A number of techniques are available from which each investigator may select those most suitable for his work. However, failure to follow certain practices, such as the use of positive and negative controls, has led to serious errors which have encumbered the literature and led to the formulation of fallacious theories.

A spring lancet or preferably a sterile needle [11] is used to draw blood either from an ear lobe or a finger. The ear lobe is preferable for it is easier to clean, and less liable to infection. The lobe is first swabbed with alcohol and then rubbed vigorously with cotton to stimulate circulation.[12] It is next punctured with lancet or needle and a few drops of blood are caught in a 13 x 100 mm. tube containing 1½ c.c. of physiological saline (.9%). These suspensions are centrifuged at 1200-1500 r.p.m. (revolutions per minute). The supernatant (that part of the fluid which floats on the surface) is drawn off and replaced with fresh saline, the resulting suspension of washed cells should be a 2% suspension, to be determined by visual inspection. All suspensions should be uniform, and all cells should be washed at least once.

Tests for the presence of group substances A and B, and M and N are made by placing one drop of the 2% cell suspension in a tube (10 x 75 mm.) to which is added one drop of the appropriate serum, anti-A, anti-B, anti-M, and anti-N. These tubes are then centrifuged one minute at 1000-1500 r.p.m. After all the tubes have been centrifuged and replaced in the tube rack, the rack of tubes is shaken until the cells of the known negative control are resuspended. The tubes may be read by simply holding them over a magnifying mirror. Each tube should be compared with a known positive and negative reaction included in the series being tested for control. Those specimens which give a positive reaction, i.e., clumping or agglutination of the cells, with the anti-A serum should next be tested with anti-A_1 serum. This subdivision of A is especially useful among aboriginal populations of the New World where presence of A_2 may indicate mixture with Caucasoid populations.

Tests for the presence of the A and B antigens may also be made on slides. For this kind of test the slide may be used to pick up a drop of blood directly from the ear, though it is preferable to transfer the blood with a loop or wooden applicator, so that there is no excess of blood. One drop should be placed at either end of the slide for the anti-A and the anti-B serum. After a drop of the serum, which

---

[11] Inexpensive expendable sterile needles with guards, each individually wrapped in paper, are now available for this purpose.

[12] In the rare event that it is not possible to draw blood from the ear lobe it may be taken in the same way as from the ear lobe from the tip of the middle finger. In cases in which the blood does not immediately appear a minute or so should be allowed to elapse before the attempt is made to express blood by pressure. Fear often produces a vaso-constrictor effect. This should be allowed to wear off before any attempt is made to obtain the blood.

should contain an anticoagulant, is added to the drop of blood the two are mixed with a toothpick and the slide is rotated to insure thorough mixing. The reaction should be easily visible to the eye.

Special care must be taken in using the anti-Rh sera owing to their considerably weaker reactions. A smaller tube (7 x 50 mm.) may be used in order to conserve sera and to facilitate reading the results in the tube by means of a microscope. When the tubes have been prepared, as in the A, B, M and N tests, by the addition of one drop of serum to one drop of 2% suspension of washed cells, the rack of tubes is placed in a pan of water and they are incubated for one hour at 37.5° C. Following this they are centrifuged at slow speed, 300-500 r.p.m. Before reading, each tube should be rotated or shaken gently to remove false agglutination. If the cells are not agglutinated they will be dispersed and resuspended, if they are agglutinated they will remain in clumps. These clumps of agglutinated cells vary in size with the strength of the reaction. It is useful to record the strength of each reaction as a check on the strength of various sera and as a not very reliable indication of homo- or hetero-zygosity. Care must be taken not to shake out a positive reaction. In the case of a person who is heterozygous, the reactions may be weaker with certain antisera (gene dose effect). All Rh tests should be read under the low power of a microscope as well as with the naked eye. This may be done by holding the tube directly under the objective, or by removing a drop of the suspension on a glass rod and placing it on a slide.

In the field where laboratory facilities are not available it is often necessary to use a stove for incubating the Rh tests. One practical method of maintaining the bath at the necessary uniform temperature is to place the tray containing the tubes over another pan of water so that the heat is derived from the steam of the lower pan of water rather than directly from the top of the stove which is subject to wide fluctuations in temperature.

For centrifuging the small Rh tubes corks may be dropped into each of the centrifuge tube jackets so that the small tubes can be easily removed.

No tests should be conducted without the use of both negative and positive controls. For this purpose it is desirable to type in advance all members of a field party. Reactions should be read twice. In this way those which are slow in developing will not be missed and an additional check on recording errors is provided. Sera should be permitted to come to room temperature before use, at all other times they should be kept in refrigeration. Diluted serum often declines in strength, consequently no more sera should be diluted for use than are needed for current typing.

Equipment

For field work certain eventualities must be anticipated which would otherwise retard the work. Sufficient glassware should be taken so that it is possible to work two or three days while tubes are drying. A good quality soap, such as Swan or Ivory, is adequate for washing the glassware. Precautions must be taken to be sure that the tubes are clean, dry and sterile.

Serum containers should be identified not only by labels but also by etching with a diamond pointed glass marking pencil. Even labels secured with cellulose tape will come off after exposure to moisture. This may happen when a boat carrying equipment ships water or when a refrigerator is inadvertently defrosted.

China marking pencils of different colors should be used to facilitate identification of individual tubes in tests employing different sera, thus, tests with anti-A serum may be marked with red and tests with anti-B serum marked with blue.

Four-tube hand operated centrifuges are available from such houses as Eimer and Amend, New York City.

Tuberculin syringes are useful for measuring small amounts of serum and saline. It is useful to weigh out salt in advance for preparing additional amounts of physiological saline in the field. This will obviate the need for carrying scales and save time.

A list of equipment is appended here, the appropriate numbers or amounts depend, of course, on the extent of the work to be done. Equipment List:

> laboratory microscope
> centrifuge
> 15 ml.* tubes
> 13 x 100 mm., 8 x 75 mm., and 7 x 50 mm. tubes
> ground glass slides
> glass rods
> expendable capillary pipettes
> 1 cc. tuberculin syringes and #22 needles
> laboratory thermometers
> alcohol
> test tube brushes
> cotton, absorbent and non-absorbent

---

* ml., milliliter, equals 1 cubic centimeter.

tube racks
expendable sterile lancets
distilled water
liter pitcher
diamond pointed glass marking pencil
magnifying mirror (shaving mirror)
colored marking pencils
beakers
soap
toothpicks
pans (for incubating and washing)
sera
corks

Collection of Bone Samples for Typing

Cancellous tissue such as that found in the bodies of the vertebrae or in the heads of the long bones is most suitable for blood typing. This can best be obtained by scraping with a bone curette. With care it is possible to remove the cancellous tissue from a vertebra without damaging its walls for measurement. The bone should be placed in a tube and made airtight. Morphological data and cultural data concerning the skeleton should be secured. Care must be taken in the case of incidental bones or mass burials that more than one specimen is not taken from one individual or that several specimens taken from one skeleton are attributed to only one.

Technique of Blood Typing Skeletons

TEST FOR THE PRESENCE OF BLOOD GROUP SUBSTANCES IN SKELETONS

This is an absorption technique which involves the application of serum of known strength to a specimen of pulverized bone. After a period of incubation the supernatant serum is drawn off the specimen and tested against fresh red cells of the appropriate group. If the group substance, which determines the blood type, is present in the specimen of bone, the antibodies of the serum are wholly or partially absorbed and the strength of the serum is thereby reduced. The consequent failure to agglutinate red cells is presumptive evidence that agglutinins were removed from the serum and therefore that the group substance was present in the skeleton tested.

The sera to be employed are titered by testing successively doubled dilutions, e.g., 1:2, 1:4, 1:8, 1:16, against a 1% suspension of fresh red cells. If 1:16 is the limiting titer, that is if it gives a $\pm$ reading whereas the next higher dilution shows no agglutination, this is taken as the end point. Counting back three dilutions, to 1:2, gives the proper dilution to be applied to the specimen. The serum should be diluted to yield a reagent with a titer of 4 to 8 units; in the example cited the serum would be diluted 2 to 4 times. Anything with a titer of less than 4 units is too weak for reliable results. These dilutions may be made in 13 x 100 mm. tubes. From each of these tubes 0.05 cc. of the diluted serum is drawn, by means of a tuberculin syringe, and placed in a 7 x 50 mm. tube, to which is added 0.05 cc. of 1% cell suspension. These are then placed in a rack and shaken at four minute intervals for thirty-two minutes. Readings of the degree of agglutination are made with the low power of a microscope. All cell suspensions should be washed, measured, and the titration should be performed before each test.

The cancellous tissue is pulverized before each test in a mortar, and 0.25 gram placed in a 13 x 100 mm. tube. Nine-tenths of a cc. of serum is added to this and the two are thoroughly mixed by rotating the tube and with a glass rod. For each skeleton tested a separate tube is prepared for the anti-A serum and for the anti-B serum. Each tube is sealed with a cork and placed in a refrigerator at 10° C. to incubate 48 hours. The tubes should be agitated at 12 hour intervals.

At the end of two days the tubes are removed from the refrigerator and permitted to return to room temperature. They are then centrifuged and the supernatant serum drawn from each by means of a tuberculin syringe with a flat ended needle. Physiological saline is added to each specimen to equal the amount drawn off and it is titrated again in three successively doubled dilutions to duplicate the original dilutions. 0.05 cc. of each dilution is placed in a blood group tube, with 0.05 cc. of 1% fresh red cell suspension and shaken as before at four minute intervals for thirty-two minutes. The results are again read with the low power of the microscope. Failure of the supernatant to agglutinate the appropriate red cells indicates that group substance of that group was present in the specimen and absorbed the agglutinins. Agglutinins should be cleared from at least two tubes, in a number of tests, for the results to be considered positive. Controls should, of course, be employed in all tests. The technique employed in testing skeletons may be found in the following papers: "Blood-Group Tests on Stains, Mummified Tissues, and Cancellous Bone," by P. B. Candela, *Am. J. Phys. Anthrop.* 25:187-214, 1939. "Blood grouping reactions of preserved bone and muscle," by L. T. Boyd and W. C. Boyd, *Am. J. Phys. Anthrop.*, 25:421-434, 1939. "A method for reducing non-specific reactions in the typing of human skeletal material," by M. P. Gray, *Am. J. Phys. Anthrop.*, n.s., *16*:135-139, 1958.

The Determination of Hemoglobins and Haptoglobins

A simple method for determining hemoglobins and haptoglobins which can be used in the field has been described by Budtz-Olsen ("Haptoglobins and haemoglobins in Australian aborigines, with a simple method for the estimation of haptoglobins," *Med. J. Austral.*, 22 Nov. 1958, 689-692).

Hemoglobins. Hemoglobin solutions are prepared by washing the red cells in saline and hemolysing them in four volumes of water and a quarter volume of toluene. Electrophoresis of the solutions is carried out on Whatman No. 3 paper, horizontally suspended in closed tanks with barbiturate buffer, 0.05, pH 8.6. The voltage used is 10 volts per centimetre at room temperature for about six hours.

Haptoglobins. Serum is collected and enough hemoglobin solution added to give a concentration of about 200 milligrams per 100 millimeters. Following several accurate estimations of this concentration in a colorimeter, simple judgment of the color by the eye alone will generally be found to be sufficiently accurate. If any of the specimens become slightly hemolysed before separation of the serum, they should be used without the addition of hemoglobin.

The details of the electrophoresis are as follows:

Apparatus. A simple tank described by Flynn and de Mayo ("Micro-electrophoresis of protein on filter paper," *The Lancet*, 2:235, 1951) with vertically suspended Whatman No. 3 paper strips is used. Other tanks will do, but owing to the longer distance between the protein fractions obtained with the Flynn and de Mayo method, haptoglobins can be determined with greater confidence with this method.

Buffer. A barbiturate-borate buffer is used. The details of preparation are as follows: 1.85 grams of barbituric acid, 10.30 grams of barbitone, 4.809 grams of boric acid, and 0.888 grams of sodium hydroxide are dissolved in two liters of water, and four millimeters of non-ionizing detergent are added. With this buffer the a_2-globulins migrate faster than in the usual barbiturate buffer and are well separated from the β-globulins, which renders the differentiation between the different haptoglobins easy. The a_1-globulins are lost in the albumin fraction, but this is unimportant for the purpose of haptoglobin determination. The detergent sharpens the bands of the different fractions, but is not otherwise essential.

Conditions of the Run. The paper is allowed to soak in the tank until the buffer is about a centimeter from the edge; 0.04 millimeter of serum is applied to the edge; the tank is closed and left for about an hour and the current is then switched on at 130 volts for 22 hours, either in a refrigerator at 5° C. or at room temperature.

Staining. After the run the paper strips are dried in an oven at 105° C., although room temperature will do. The strips are then soaked for 10 minutes in a solution of 0.2 gram of benzidine and a small crystal of sodium nitroprusside in 15 millimeters of methanol with four drops of glacial acetic acid. This solution is washed off with a solution of one volume of 3% hydrogen peroxide, one volume of ether and two volumes of methanol, and the color is then developed with this solution for two or three minutes. The paper strips are washed in gently running tap water for about half an hour. The blue color is permanent.

The distinctions between the three haptoglobins depend entirely upon the distance moved by the particular haptoglobins. For ease of judgment a known group 2-1 should always be run with the unknown.

Anthropometric Recording Blanks

Printed blanks for the recording of anthropometric, anthroposcopic, physiometric, and morphological measurements greatly facilitate the processes of recording and analysis of data. Typical blanks are here reprinted through the courtesy of Dr. J. L. Angel.

CRANIOMETRY

Why Measure Skulls?

For several generations physical anthropologists measured skulls in the belief that thereby they were likely to obtain results which would enable them to trace the relationships between the races of mankind. It was believed that the form of the skull in particular remained constant in each race, and that different races typically showed different cranial indices. Hence, all one had to do was to measure skulls, calculate the indices, and draw the more or less "obvious" conclusions. Unfortunately for this rather naïve belief there are several crucial objections to it. In the first place the form of the head is now known to be subject to change through environmental influences. In the second place there are great differences in intragroup variability in all measurements and indices among the ethnic groups of mankind. In the third place closely related groups

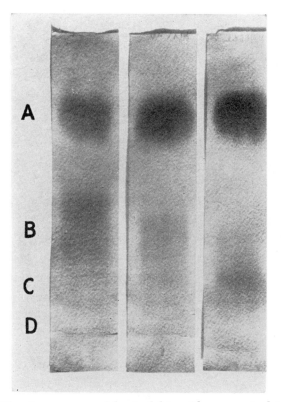

Figure 11. The three groups of haptoglobins. The group is determined by the distance moved by the haptoglobin. A, albumin; B, haptoglobins; C, position of globulins; D, point of application. (Courtesy, Dr. O. E. Budtz-Olsen.)

and individuals frequently exhibit considerable differences in cranial measurements and indices, while more distantly related groups and individuals exhibit striking likenesses. Finally, the cephalic index of a whole group will change in the course of time as the trend towards brachycephalization in man abundantly shows. Why then, it may well be asked, measure skulls? The answer is: Precisely in order to obtain this kind of knowledge, and in order to be able to give as accurate a description of a skull or group of skulls as possible. In addition, in studies of the micro-evolutionary process analysis of craniometric data for neighboring populations or segments of the same population may yield valuable results.[13]

---

[13] See W. S. Laughlin and J. B. Jørgensen, Isolate variation in Greenlandic Eskimo crania. *Acta Genetica et Statistica Medica*, 6:3-12, 1956.

ANTHROPOMETRY and MORPHOLOGY

Name............ Age...... Place............ Area............ Field number............

Sex............ Birthdate............ Examined: Date............ Time............ Observer............

Related to:............ Appearance............ Occupation............ Birthplace............ Ancestry............

Father's name............ Birthplace............ Age if living............ Died at age?............ Cause of death

Mother's name............ Appearance............ Skills............ Birthplace............ Age if living............ Died at age?............ Cause of death

Brothers............
Sisters............
Stillbirths............
Single?............ Married?............ At age?............ Divorced?............ Widowed?............ Birth rank............
Boys............
Girls............ Childhood............
Diet............ Breakfast............ Lunch............ Supper............

Occupation............ Religion............
Social status............ Economic status............ Biographical............
Illnesses at age ?............ Housing............ Handedness............
.... Film number............
.... Recorder............ Frames............

Weight............	Bi-auricular breadth............
	Bizygomatic breadth............
Stature............	Bigonial breadth............
Acromion height............	Total face height............
Trochanter height............	Upper face height............
Tibiale height............	Chin height............
Sphyrion height............	Nose height............
Span............	
Sitting height............	Nose breadth............
Foot length............	Interorbital............
Foot breadth............	Biorbital............
Humerus length............	
Radius length............	Mouth breadth............
Hand length............	Ear height............
Hand breadth............	Ear breadth............
Biacromial............	
Bi-iliac............	Stature ∛Weight............
Chest breadth............	Relative sitting height............
Chest depth............	Relative chest circumference............
Abdomen depth............	Relative shoulder breadth............
Chest circumference............	Thoracic index............
	Hand, L-Br. index............
Head circumference............	
Head length............	Cephalic index............
Nasion-occipital length............	Mean height index............
Head breadth............	Fronto-parietal............
Auricular-vertex height............	Cranio-facial............
Auricular-nasion length............	Fronto-gonial............
	Facial index............
Minimum frontal breadth............	Upper facial index............
	Nasal index............

Pale Pink 3 "White" Brunet 7–9 Swarthy 10, 11 R. br 12–14, 16 Lt. br. 15, 17, 18 Lt. y. br. 4, 5 Y. br. 19–20, 6 Md. br. 21–25 Choc. 26–29 Dk. br. 30–35 Black 36	++ Freckles None Few + ++ Moles None Few + ++	Deep waves Curly Frizzly Woolly Texture Fine + Coarse Wiry Quantity Sm. + ++	+ ++ Beard quantity Ssm. Sm. + ++ Body hair Abs. Sl. + ++	Dk. br. 4–5 Brown 7–9 Red br. 6, 10 Gld. br. 11–16 Ash br. 22–26 Golden 17–19 Ash 20, 21 Red 1–3 Grey, sl. Grey, + White Red pigment Abs. Pres:	Dk.-lt. br. Lt. brown Green-br. Grey-br. Blue-br. Green Grey Blue Other Unmatched	Sl. + ++ Mixed eyes +++ dark ++ dark Even ++ light +++ light Pigment dots Abs. Pres:	Zoned Scalloped Diffuse Spotted Conjunctiva Clear Yellow Grey Bloodshot Orbit height Low + High	Internal Sl. + ++ Median Sl. + ++ External Sl. + ++ Complete:
Palpebral slit Down Horiz. Up sl. Up + Up ++ Opening ht. Sm. + ++ Eyebrow thickness Sl. + ++ +++	Concurrency Abs. Sl. + ++ Temp. hair jct. Abs. Sl. + ++ Browridges Ssm. Sm. + ++	Nasion depr. Trace Sl. + ++ +++ Bony profile Straight Concave Wavy Convex Salience Sl. + ++	Root height Sm. + ++ +++ (ssm.) Root breadth Ssm. (+++) Sm + ++ Bridge height Sm. + ++ +++ (ssm.)	Bridge breadth Ssm. (+++) Sm. + ++ Tip thickness Ssm. (+++) Sm. + ++ Tip shape Pointed Bilobed Angular Rounded Blobby Snub	Septum tilt Up + Up sl. Horiz. Down sl. Down + Nostril form Slit Ellipse Intermed. Round Visibility, lat. None Sl. + ++	Vis., frontal None Sl. + ++ Nostril axes Parallel Obl. sl. Oblique + Transverse Alae Compressed + Flaring Extended	Lip thickness V. thin (+++) Thin + ++ Eversion Sl. + ++ +++ Lip seam Abs. Sl. + ++	Integ. lips Thin + Thick Alv. prognathism Abs. (+++) Sl. + ++ Chin projection Negative Neutral Sl. + ++
Chin type Median Triangle Bilateral Malars Anterior proj. Abs. (+++) Sl. + ++ Lateral proj. Compr. Sl. + ++ +++	Gonia eversion Compr. Sl. + ++ +++ Ear projection Sl. + ++ Helix Flat Sl roll + ++	Anti-helix Sl. + ++ Darwin's pt. Abs. Pres: Ear sinus Abs. Pres: Lobe None Soldered Attached Free Long & free	Temp. fullness Flat Sl. + Lambd. flat. None Sl. + ++ Occ. curve Flat Sl. + ++	Blood type A, B, O: M, N Rh′-C: Rho-D: Rh″-E:	P-T-C Taste-blind Tastes: Tongue-roll Abs. Pres: Trilling Abs. Pres. Th-sound Abs. Pres.	Somatotype Temperament Nutrit. state Menarche *or* Voice-change Pulse rate	Asymmetry Pathology	Type
Tooth eruption Incomplete Complete M₁ suppr. Other No. teeth lost No. teeth carious Teeth wear None Sl. + ++ +++	Crowding None Sl. + ++ Pyorrhea None Sl. + ++ Absorption None Sl. + ++	Palate height Low + ++ +++ Palate form Parabolic Elliptical Hyperbolic V Small U Broad U Palatine torus Absent Ridge: Mound: Lump:	Shovel Is. Abs. Sl. + ++ Upper cusp no Lower cusp no. Teeth rotated Central trema	Molar pattern Plus Dryopith. Bite Under Edge Sl. over + over ++ over Accessory cusps Teeth size	Left Dentition Right 8 7 6 5 4 3 2 1 1 2 3 4 5 6 7 8 X: missing *: carious s: suppressed m: milk tooth retained w: worn down to roots			

Figure 12. Recording blank for anthropometry and morphology of the living. (Courtesy, Dr. P. L. Angel.)

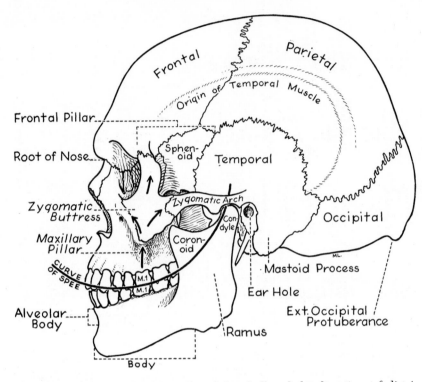

Figure 13. Showing the buttresses of the skull and the directions of distribution of the forces transmitted from the lower first through the upper first molar tooth.

The importance of craniometry in the description and analysis of the remains of fossil man and other primates is obvious; in the comparative study of the primates it is an indispensable tool, as it is in growth studies of the skull, the growth of the dental apparatus, in the study of the character and relationships of individuals and departed populations which are known mainly or solely from their cranial remains, in forensic medicine, in the identification of persons from their crania, and finally when the genetics of the skull comes to be thoroughly studied, as it must, craniometric techniques will become increasingly indispensable.

Definitions

Skull. In practice this term is commonly used with the following two interchangeable meanings, (1) the skeleton of the braincase, face, and lower jaw, (2) the skeleton of the braincase and face without the lower jaw. To this double usage there is no objection, though strictly speaking the term is by most anthropologists and anatomists defined in the first sense.

Cranium. Used with the same meanings as *skull.*

Calvarium. The skull minus the lower jaw.

Calvaria. The braincase minus facial bones and the lower jaw.

Calva or Calotte. The skull cap, i.e., the top of the braincase or calvaria minus its base.

Landmarks

There has, in the past, been a great superfluity of landmarks on the skull, most of which have rarely been used. Only those which are in most common use will be defined here. The customary abbreviations printed in parentheses.

Braincase

1. *Glabella* (gl). The most prominent point on the middle of the frontal bone between the superciliary arches (supraorbital ridges) and above the nasofrontal suture.

2. *Bregma* (br). The point of intersection of the coronal and sagittal sutures.

3. *Opisthocranion* (op). The most distant (posterior) point on the skull from the glabella in the mid-sagittal plane, excluding the external occipital protuberance or inion.

4. *Inion* (in). The base of the external occipital protuberance in the mid-sagittal plane.

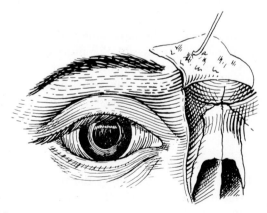

Figure 14. Showing the relationship of the nasion to the superior palpebral sulcus.

5. *Opisthion* (o). The median point on the posterior margin of the occipital foramen.

6. *Basion* (ba). The median point on the anterior margin of the occipital foramen.

7. *Porion* (po). The highest middle point on the margin of the external auditory meatus.

Facial Skeleton

8. *Nasion* (na). The mid-point of the naso-frontal suture.

9. *Nasospinale* (ns). The point at which a line tangent to the lower margins of the nasal aperture is intersected by the mid-sagittal plane. Since the base of the anterior nasal spine usually prevents actual instrumental contact with this point, it is usual to take the measurement at the level of the nasospinale somewhat to one side and deduct the two or three millimeters from the final measurement.

10. *Prosthion* (pr). The most antero-inferior point on the maxilla between the upper central incisor teeth.

11. *Maxillofrontale* (mf). The point of intersection of the anterior lacrimal crest with the frontomaxillary suture.

12. *Infradentale* (id). The most antero-superior point on the alveolar margin between the lower central incisors on the lower jaw.

13. *Gnathion* (gn). The middle point on the lower border of the mandible.

14. *Gonion* (go). The most lateral external point of junction of the horizontal and ascending rami of the lower jaw.

15. *Ectomolare* (ecm). The most lateral point on the outer surface of the alveolar margins, usually opposite the middle of the second molar tooth.

16. *Endomolare* (enm). The most lateral point on the inner surface of the lingual margins of the alveolar processes, usually opposite the middle of the lingual surfaces of the second molar teeth.

17. *Orale* (ol). The point in the bony palate where the mid-sagittal plane bisects a line drawn tangentially to the point of maximum convexity of the lingual margins of the alveoli for the two central incisor teeth.

General Comments

It should always be remembered that the best preserved of skulls is a fragile and valuable object. It should therefore always be handled with considerable care. There is something about the gaping orbits of the skull which seems universally to suggest that it be picked up by introducing the thumb in one orbit and several fingers in the other.

This is invariably fatal to the papyrus-thin bones of the medial orbital walls. Hence, all persons likely to handle skulls must be instructed never to handle a skull in this manner, and they should be similarly instructed never to lift it by the zygomatic arches. The skull is best handled with one hand at the supratemporal crests or at the occipito-parietal regions. Teeth are extremely fragile, and the enamel is easily cracked and chipped. Loose teeth should be firmly glued into the sockets in which their roots belong.

In measuring skulls a moderately soft doughnut shaped pad 1½ inches thick with an outside diameter 8½ inches, and an internal diameter of 3¼ inches will be found useful upon which to rest the skull in any desired position. A cloth bag 8 by 8 inches or more, filled with rice or sand is preferred by many workers. A puncture-proof small toy rubber tire, 7 x 1½ inches, forms an excellent rest for a skull.[14]

Instruments should be frequently checked for accuracy, and each measurement should be made in a uniform manner. It is important to record the technique used in making each measurement and to make this record an intrinsic part of the report of these measurements, whether the report is intended for publication or not.

Cranial Measurements

1. *Maximum cranial Length* (Spreading Caliper). From glabella to opisthocranion.

2. *Maximum Cranial Breadth* (Spreading Caliper). At right angles to the mid-sagittal plane wherever maximum breadth is found, above the level of the supramastoid crests or posterior roots of the zygomatic arches and the regions below.

3. *Basion-Bregma Height* (Spreading Caliper). From basion to bregma.

4. *Minimum Frontal Cranial Breadth* (Spreading Caliper). Minimum breadth between the temporal crests on the frontal bone.

5. *Maximum Bizygomatic Breadth* (Spreading Caliper). The greatest breadth between the two zygomatic arches.

6. *Total Cranial Facial Height* (Sliding Compass). From gnathion to nasion.

7. *Upper Cranial Facial Height* (Sliding Compass). From prosthion to nasion.

8. *Basion-Prosthion Line* (Sliding Compass or Spreading Caliper). From basion to prosthion.

9. *Nasal Height* (Sliding Compass). From nasion to the mean of

---

[14] The "Clipper" supplied by R.C.A. Rubber Co., Akron, Ohio.

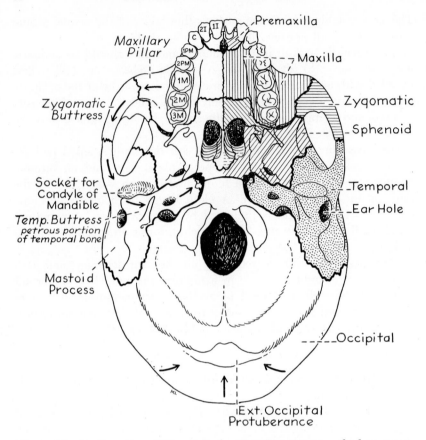

Figure 15. Basilar view of the skull showing directions in which compressive strains transmitted through the first upper molar (1M) are taken up by the zygomatic buttress, while those from the back of the skull pass down toward the external occipital protuberance.

the lowest points on the lower borders of the nasal aperture (the subnasale) on each side of the nasal spine.

10. *Nasal Breadth* (Sliding Compass). The maximum distance between the lateral margins of the nasal aperture perpendicular to the mid-sagittal plane.

11. *Upper Nasal Breadth* (Sliding Compass). The distance between the points of juncture of the naso-frontal and naso-maxillary sutures on the right and left sides.

12. *Lower Nasal Breadth* (Sliding Compass). The distance be-

tween the points at which the naso-maxillary suture terminates at the nasal aperture on the left and right sides.

13. *Orbital Breadth* (Sliding Compass). Owing to the variability in the conformation and orientation of the orbits these are conventionally treated as rectangles. The horizontal axis being determined by an imaginary line running from maxillofrontale to the middle of the lateral orbital border (ectoconchion). Right and left orbits are recorded separately.

14. *Orbital Height* (Sliding Compass). The maximum height from the upper to the lower orbital borders perpendicular to the horizontal axis of the orbit.

15. *Interorbital Breadth* (Sliding Compass). The distance between the right and left maxillofrontale.

16. *Bi-Orbital Breadth* (Sliding Compass). From the middle of one lateral orbital border (ectoconchion) to the other.

17. *Maxillo-Alveolar Length* (Sliding Compass). From prosthion to the points of bisection of a line tangent to the posterior terminal borders of the alveolar processes (maxillary tuberosities).

18. *Maxillo-Alveolar Breadth* (Sliding Compass). Maximum distance from one external lateral alveolar border to the other, usually opposite the second molar teeth. (ectomolare).

19. *Mean Diameter of Foramen Magnum* (Sliding Compass). Maximum length from basion to opisthion, and maximum transverse diameter.

20. *Bi-Condylar Width* (Sliding Compass). Distance between the most external points on the condyles of the lower jaw.

21. *Symphyseal Height* (Sliding Compass). Distance between gnathion and infradentale.

22. *Bigonial Diameter* (Sliding Compass). Distance between right and left gonion points.

23. *Height of Ascending Left Mandibular Ramus* (Measuring Board or Sliding Compass). Usually taken with a specially designed hinged measuring board from which the height of the ramus may be read directly from the base of the ramus to the highest point on the left condyle. In the absence of a measuring board, from left gonion to the highest point on the left condyle.

24. *Minimum Breadth of Left Ascending Mandibular Ramus* (Sliding Compass). Least distance between the anterior and posterior borders of the left ramus perpendicular to its height.

25. *Maximum Cranial Circumference* (Steel Tape). Above the

level of the brow ridges around the most distant projection of the occiput to the zero point anteriorly.

26. *Transverse Cranial Arc* (Steel Tape). From left porion across bregna to right porion.

27. *The Frankfurt Horizontal* (FH) *Plane.* The horizontal plane of the skull determined by the right and left porion and the lowest point on the inferior margin of, preferably, the left orbit (orbitale). The skull is usually oriented in this plane when measurements taken in a constant plane are to be made, or when craniograms, photographs, or other illustrations are to be made for comparative or illustrative purposes.

28. *Auricular Height.* This important measurement may be taken with Todd's Head Spanner or the Western Reserve Craniostat. Both instruments are provided with a simple device for determining the Frankfurt Horizontal plane. Measurements are read directly. Ranke's or Mollison's craniophor require the determination of bi-porionic breadth and the distance of each porion from the bregma. The vertical section of the triangle thus formed yields auricular height.

29. *Cranial Capacity.* Cranial capacity has been measured in a variety of ways and the results obtained are not always strictly comparable, hence it is extremely important to know when comparing figures for cranial capacity obtained from the literature what method was used. The most usual procedure is to fill the cranial cavity with some material which will easily conform to the internal irregularities and spaces of the braincase. Mustard seed or small shot is frequently used, the material being thoroughly distributed by agitating the skull either in one's hands or in an apparatus specially devised for the purpose. When the skull is securely filled the contents are then poured into a cubic centimeter measuring glass which is then agitated until it is thoroughly packed and the reading taken directly. Alternatively the mustard seed may be weighed and multiplied by a factor to give volume. Methods such as this avoid the possibility of error when the measuring glass is used. Formulae which give satisfactory results have been worked out by different investigators for several groups. The best of these formulae for determining cranial capacity are the following, where L is cranial length, H is auricular height, H' basion-bregmatic height, and B cranial breadth. L is multiplied by B, and the product multiplied by H or H':

$$\text{Female Capacity } .000375 \times \text{LBH} + 296.40$$

All Races: Male Capacity $.000365 \times \text{LBH} - 359.34$ (Pearson)
Negroids: Capacity $.0003849 \times \text{LBH} + 96 \pm 65/\sqrt{N}$ (Isserlis)

Australoids: Capacity .000263 × LBH' + 404.9 ± 35.1/√N (von Bonin)
Caucasoids: Capacity .000366 × LBH + 198.9 (Hooke)[15]

Craniometric Indices

30. The Cranial Index

	Max Breadth × 100
	Max. Length
Dolichocranic	×—74.9
Mesocranic	75.0—79.9
Brachycranic	80.0—84.9
Hyperbrachycranic	85.0—89.9

31. Cranial Length-Height Index

	Basion-Bregma Height × 100
	Max. Length
Chamaecranic	×—69.9
Orthocranic	70.0—74.9
Hypsicranic	75.0—×

32. Cranial Breadth-Height Index

	Basion-Bregma Height × 100
	Max. Breadth
Tapeinocranic	×—91.9
Metriocranic	92.0—97.9
Acrocranic	98.0—×

33. Total Facial Index

	Nasion-Gnathion Height × 100
	Bizygomatic Breadth
Hypereuryprosopic	×—79.9
Euryprosopic	80.0—84.9
Mesoprosopic	85.0—89.9
Leptoprosopic	90.0—94.9
Hyperleptoprosopic	95.0—×

34. Upper Facial Index

	Nasion-Prosthion Height × 100
	Bizygomatic Breadth
Hypereuryene	×—44.9
Euryene	45.0—49.9
Mesene	50.0—54.9
Leptene	55.0—59.9
Hyperleptene	60.0—×

[15] For further details see Hambly, W. D.: Cranial capacities, A study in Methods, *Fieldiana Anthropology* (Chicago Natural History Museum), *36*:25-75, 1947.

35. Nasal Index

$$\frac{\text{Max. Nasal Breadth of Nasal Aperture} \times 100}{\text{Nasion-Nasospinale Height}}$$

Leptorrhine	×—46.9
Mesorrhine	47.0—50.9
Chamaerrhine	51.0—57.9
Hyperchamaerrhine	58.0—×

36. Orbital Index

$$\frac{\text{Max. Orbital Breadth} \times 100}{\text{Max. Orbital Length}}$$

Chamaeconch	×—75.9
Mesoconch	76.0—84.9
Hypsiconch	85.0—×

37. Palatal Index

$$\frac{\text{Max. Palatal Breadth} \times 100}{\text{Max. Palatal Length}}$$

Leptostaphyline	×—79.9
Mesostaphyline	80.0—84.9
Brachystaphyline	85.0—×

38. Maxillo-Alveolar Index

$$\frac{\text{Bi-Ectomolare Breadth} \times 100}{\text{Maxillo-Alveolar Length}}$$

Dolichuranic	×—109.9
Mesuranic	110.0—114.9
Brachyuranic	115.0—×

Estimating Age of Skull

During the process of growth and development the skull shows, within broad limits, certain relatively constant changes which may be used as criteria of age. Since there is an appreciable amount of variability both in the order and time of eruption of the teeth, these features must be utilized with caution in the aging of a skull up to the age of 25 years.

Approximate Age of Tooth Eruption

Deciduous or Milk Dentition

Lower Central Incisors	5 to 12 months
Upper Incisors	6 to 14 months
Lower Lateral Incisors	8 to 20 months
First Molars	13 to 20 months

| Canines | 13 to 30 months |
| Second Molars | 18 to 38 months |

Permanent Dentition

First Molars	6th year
Central Incisors	7th year
Lateral Incisors	8th year
First Premolars	9th year
Second Premolars	10th year
Canines	11th to 12th year
Second Molars	12th to 13th year
Third Molars	17th to 25th year

The deciduous or milk teeth number 20 and the deciduous dental formula is written in minuscule letters i $\frac{2}{2}$, c $\frac{1}{1}$, m $\frac{2}{2}$ (incisors 2, canines 1, molars 2, on each side and in each jaw). It is to be noted that no premolars are present in the deciduous dentition. The formula for the permanent dentition is written in capital letters I $\frac{2}{2}$, C $\frac{1}{1}$, PM $\frac{2}{2}$, M $\frac{3}{3}$.

The closure or obliteration of the sutures on the external surfaces of the skull constitutes another fairly useful means of aging the skull. The standards for estimating age of the skull from suture closure have been worked out principally by Todd and Lyon on whites and Negroes in whom the pattern and time of closure appears to be much the same.[16] The variability in the closure of most of these sutures is, however, so great that too great reliance should not be based on this form of aging the skull.

The medio-frontal suture through which sutural junction between the two hemi-frontal bones is established in the infant skull usually commences to obliterate at the level of the frontal eminences during the latter half of the first year. The process of obliteration proceeds towards the bregma, and by the conclusion of the second year the greater part of the suture is obliterated. A small supra-nasal portion remains unobliterated till the sixth year, though remnants of this may persist into adult life. The whole medio-frontal suture remains unobliterated in about 8.5 per cent of Caucasoids, 1.2 per cent of Negroids, and in less than 1.0 per cent of Australoids. When the medio-frontal suture remains unobliterated *after* its normal period of closure it is known as the *metopic* suture, and the condition it thus constitutes is called *metopism*. Metopism is sometimes a familial trait, and by the unwary is occasionally mistaken as evidence of a fracture

---

[16] Todd, T. W. and Lyon, D. W.: Ectocranial closure in adult males of white stock. *Am. J. Phys. Anthropol.*, 8:23-46; 47-71; 149-168, 7:325-384, 1925.

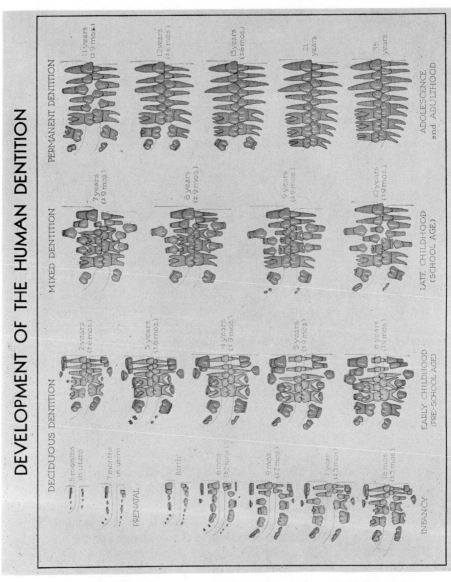

Figure 16. Development of the human dentition. (Courtesy, Drs. I. Schour and M. Massler and the American Dental Association.)

The seven unossified areas in the membrane between the bones known as fontanelles undergo closure in the following order:

Sagittal: (Situated at the obelion) At birth or before the fourth month.

Posterior: (Situated at apex of occipital bone) Two months after birth.

Antero-Lateral: (Paired. At pterion) Three months after birth.

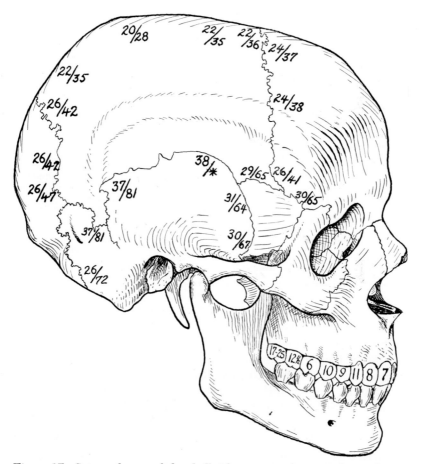

Figure 17. Suture closure of the skull. The superior figures indicate the age at which the portion of the suture commences to obliterate, the inferior figures the age at which obliteration is completed. The * indicates that the suture never completely closes. The figures on the upper teeth give the usual ages in years of the eruption of each permanent tooth. Owing to the great variability involved these figures must be used with caution.

TABLE II

ECTOCRANIAL SUTURE CLOSURE IN MALES

Suture	Commencement and Course	Termination or Peak	General Rate
Sagittal (s)	22 ⎫	35	slows at 31 at 3.9
Spheno-frontal, lesser	22 ⎪	64	slows at 30 at 3.0 final burst of activity.
	⎬ Slow		
Spheno-frontal, greater	22 ⎪ to 26		slows at 30 at 3.0 final burst of activity
Coronal (c) 1 and 2	24 ⎭	38	slows at 29 at 3.4
Coronal 3	26 ⎫	41	slows at 29 at 2.1
Lambdoid (L) 1 and 2	26 ⎪ rapid	42	slows at 31 at 3.4
Lambdoid 3	26 ⎬ to ca. 30	47	slows at 30 at 2.2
Masto-occipital 3	26 ⎭	72	32–48 at 3.2, slow progress thereafter
Spheno-parietal	29 ⎫	65	29–46 at 30 slow progress thereafter.
Spheno-temporal 2	30 ⎪ slow at	67	at 3.9 gradual progress
Spheno-temporal 1	31 ⎬ once	67	at 2.4 31–62 at 0.5 burst of activity at 63
Masto-occipital 1 and 2	30 ⎭	81	32–45 at 1.25 activity between 46 and 64.
Parieto-mastoid 1 and 2	37 ⎫	81	almost inactive till 50 slow progress thereafter
Squamous posterior	37 ⎬ almost inactive till 62	81	burst of activity at 63 burst of activity at 79
Squamous anterior	37 ⎭	81	at 3.2 burst of activity at 63 burst of activity at 79

Numbers such as 3.9, 3.0, 2.2, and the like, refer to extent of suture closure in fourths, with 0 for no suture closure, 1 for one-fourth of the total suture closure, 3 for three-fourths of the total suture closure, and 4 for complete suture closure. Age in years.

Postero-Lateral: (Paired. At posterior-inferior angle of parietal bone) End of the first year.

Bregmatic: (Situated at bregma) During the second year.

During the second year the halves of the mandible unite at the symphysis, and the mastoid process appears.

At birth the occipital bone consists of four parts: an upper or squamous portion, two lateral portions, and a basilar part. The squama unites with the lateral parts between the third and fifth years; the lateral parts with the basi-occipital during the fourth or fifth years. The basi-occipital is united to the basi-sphenoid by a strip of cartilage. The area it occupies is known as the basilar suture. This undergoes obliteration between the age of 18 and 25 years.

External or ectocranial suture closure exhibits much variability, but taken together with other features of the skull it provides a useful additional means of arriving at an age estimate of the skull. In Figure

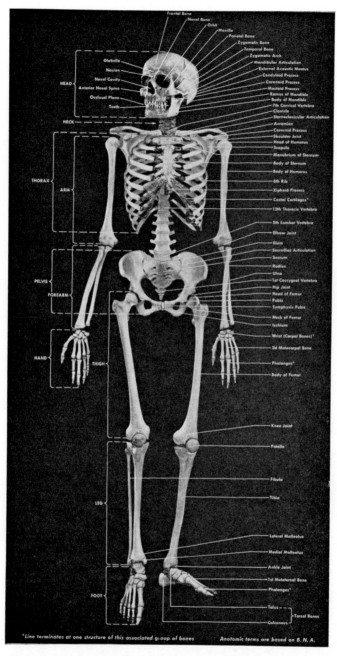

Figure 18. The Human skeleton. (Courtesy, Eastman Kodak Co., Rochester, New York.)

CRANIAL MEASUREMENTS and MORPHOLOGICAL OBSERVATIONS

Field number.........	Sex.........	Date.........	Observer.........
Area.........	Site.........	Group.........	Period.........
Age.........	Muscularity.........	Weight.........	Sex criteria.........
Description.........	Condition.........	Anomalies.........	Type.........

Glabello-occipital length.........	Optic foramen-nasion.........	Frontal angle.........	Left orbital index.........
Nasion-occipital.........	Optic foramen-basion.........	Forehead slope angle.........	External palatal.........
Basion-bregma height.........	Sphenobasion-nasion.........	Nasalia profile angle.........	Cranial capacity.........
Forehead height.........	Sphenobasion-basion.........	Facial angle.........	Skull module.........
Nasion-bregma chord.........	Sphenobasion-alveolon.........	Alveolar angle.........	Vault module.........
Bregma-lambda chord.........	External palate length.........	Orbit sagittal angle.........	
Lambda-opisthion chord.........	External palate breadth.........	Orbit droop angle.........	Stature.........
Lambda-inion chord.........	Palate height (M₁–M₁).........	Orbit a-p axis angle.........	Asymmetry or Deformation.........
Inion-opisthion chord.........	Orbit height, L–R.........	Nasal floor angle.........	Kind.........
Frontal arc.........	Orbit breadth, L–R.........	Alveolar plane angle.........	Degree.........
Parietal arc.........	Biorbital breadth.........	Mandibular plane angle.........	Cause.........
Occipital arc.........	Interorbital breadth.........	Chin profile angle.........	Vault.........
Sagittal arc.........	Dakryon-nasion salient.........	Opisthion-lambda angle.........	Ill-filled.........
Horizontal circumference.........	Upper nasalia breadth.........	Foramen magnum angle.........	Medium.........
Transverse arc.........	Lower nasalia breadth.........	Basi-occipital angle.........	Well-filled.........
Porion-temporal lines.........	Nose breadth.........	Auricular-vertex height.........	Norma verticalis.........
Maximum vault breadth.........	Nose height.........	Auricular-bregma height.........	Spheroid.........
Maximum frontal breadth.........	Nasalia length.........	Auricular-nasion length.........	Ellipsoid.........
Minimum frontal breadth.........	Nasion-prosthion height.........	Auricular-infraorbitale.........	Ovoid.........
Bi-auricular breadth.........	Nasion-menton height.........	Auricular-basion height.........	Byrsoid.........
Bi-mastoid breadth.........	Incisor height.........	Cranial index.........	Sphenoid.........
Bizygomatic breadth.........	Incisor overlap (vertical).........	Mean auricular height index.........	Square.........
Bi-stylomastoid breadth.........	Incisor overshoot (horiz.).........	Fronto-parietal index.........	Rhomboid.........
Least bi-sphenoid.........	Chin height.........	Bi-auricular-parietal index.........	Pentagonoid.........
Foramen magnum, L. & Br..........	Bicondylar breadth.........	Basal length-breadth index.........	Norma Lateralis.........
Left carotid foramen a-p.........	Bigonial breadth.........		Ellipsoid.........
Left parietal thickness.........	Bi-mental breadth.........	Cranio-facial index.........	Ovoid.........
Porion-mastoid height.........	Gonion-symphysion length.........	Zygo-frontal index.........	Pentagonoid.........
Zygoma thickness.........	Direct ramus height.........	Fronto-gonial index.........	Round.........
Articular eminence salient.........	Minimum ramus breadth.........	Zygo-gonial index.........	Square.........
Articular eminence a-p.........	Corpus thickness (M₁).........	Facial index.........	Sphenoid.........
Basion-nasion length.........	Molar length.........	Upper facial index.........	Norma occipitalis.........
Basion-prosthion length.........	Mandibular angle.........	Nasal index.........	Spheroid.........
			Rounded.........
			Gabled.........
			Hausform.........
			Hayrick.........
			Barrel-vault.........
			Ellipsoid.........
			Norma facialis.........
			Rounded.........
			Heart.........
			Pentagonoid.........
			Squat hexagon.........
			Long hexagon.........
			Square.........
			Rectangular.........
			Trapezoid.........
			Triangular.........

FIGURE 19. Recording blank for measurements and morphological observations on the skull. (Courtesy, Dr. J. L. Angel.)

TEMPORAL / PARIETAL / BASE / FACE Recording Form

Divided
Continuous
Browridge size
Sm. + ++ +++
Metopism
Traces
Complete
Frontal grooves
Trace – sl. + – ++

Frontal bosses
Sm. + ++ +++
Median crest
Sm. +++
PARIETAL
Postcoronal depr.
Sl. + +++

Parietal bosses
Sm. + ++ +++
Pterion type   Left   Right
H   H
X   X
Retourné   Retourné

Crest size
Trace
Sm. + ++
Crest shape
Ridge
Mound
SUTURE SERRATION
Coronal
Sagittal
Lambdoid

Begin
++
Complete
Sagittal
Open
Begin
++
Complete
Squamous
+
Complete

Suborbital fossa
None
Sl.
Malar size
Sm. + ++ +++
Lateral projection
Compressed
Sl.

TEMPORAL
Fullness
Sl. + ++
Curve
Flat
Sl. ++
Mastoids
Sm. + +++
Supramastoid crest

BASE
Condyle projection
Sl. + +++
Pharyngeal tubercle
Sm. +
Pharyngeal fossa
Sm. +
Petrous depression
Sl. + +++

Styloid size
Sm. + +++
Tympanic plate
Thin +
Thick
Postglenoid process
Short +
Long
Eminence slope
Sl. + ++

Auditory meatus
Round
Oval
Ellipse
Slit
Angular spine
Sm. + +++
Ext. pterygoid plate
Sm. +
Pterygo-spinous for.

Postnatal spine
Sm. + ++
Orbit shape
Ellipsoid
Square
Rectangular
Rhomboid
Sm. +
Lacrimal foramen
Sm. +
Infraorbital suture
Absent
Present:

FACE
Palate shape
Parabolic
Elliptical
Hyperbolic (V)
Small U
Large U
Palatine torus
None
Sm. +
Pal. torus form
Ridge
Mound
Lump
Palate height:

Anterior projection
Sl. +
Marginal process
Sm. + ++
Nose root height
Low
V. low +
High
V. high
Nasion depression
Sl. + ++

Nose root breadth
V. narrow
Narrow +
Wide
V. wide
Bridge height
V. low
Low +
High
V. high
Bridge breadth
Narrow ++

Nose profile
Straight
Concave
Wavy
Convex
"Classical profile"
Absent
Present
Nasal spine size
Absent
Sm. + +++
Nasal spine form
Pointed
Spatulate
Downturned

Nasal sills
None
Dull +
Sharp
Subnasal grooves
None
Sl. + ++
Prognathism (total)
None
Sl. + +++

Alveolar prognathism
Maxilla   Mandible
None   None
Sl.   Sl.
+   +
+++   +++
Mouth region form
Linear
Tilted
Angular
Civilized
Infantile
Squat
Primitive
Other

Chin form
Median
Triangular
Bilateral
Chin projection
Negative
Neutral
Sl. +
Genial tubercles
None
Pit
Sm. +

Mylo-hyoid ridge
Sm. +
Pterygoid insertion
Sl.
Gonia eversion
None
Sl. +
Mandibular torus
Absent
Present:

Tooth eruption
Incomplete:
Complete
Suppr. all M_3s
Suppr.:
Other
Alveolar absorption
None
Sl. + ++
Pyorrhea
None
Sl. + ++

No. alveolae present
No. teeth lost p.m.
No. teeth lost a.m.
No. teeth carious
No. abscesses

Abscess size
Sm. + ++
Teeth wear
None
Sl. +++
Crowding
None
Sl. ++

Teeth quality
V. poor
Poor +
Good
Excellent
Molar cusps (number)
Upper
Lower
Molar cusp pattern
Plus
Dryopithecus
Accessory cusps
None
Present:

Shovel incisors
Absent
Sl. ++
Bite
Under
Edge
Sl. over
+ over
Central trema
Absent
Sl. ++

	Dentition	
Left		Right
8 7 6 5 4 3 2 1		1 2 3 4 5 6 7 8

Crown L. & Br.: M_2 M_1
Upper
Lower

/: alveolus missing   *: carious   m: milk tooth
=: lost post mortem   a: abscess   retained
X: lost ante mortem   s: suppr.   w: worn to roots

Figure 19—Continued

17 the age at which various parts of the cranial sutures commence to obliterate and the course and direction of the obliterative process is also shown.

In old age the skull bones are usually somewhat thinner, and the skull tends to be appreciably lighter and more fragile owing to the absorption of spongious bone and the associated extension and enlargement of the sinuses.

The state of closure of the following ectocranial sutures yield a *rough* assessment of age.

I. Vault sutures

    1. Coronal (bregmatic, complicated, and pteric portions)
    2. Sagittal (bregmatic, vertex, obelion, and lambdoid portions)
    3. Lambdoid (lambdoid, medial, and asterionic portions)

II. Circum-meatul sutures

    1. Squamous (anterior and posterior parts)
    2. Parieto-mastoid (superior and inferior parts)
    3. Masto-occipital (posterior, middle, and anterior parts)
    4. Spheno-temporal
    5. Spheno-frontal (greater and lesser wings)

Sutures on the exterior of the skull (ectocranial sutures) will not alone serve to give a reliable estimate of age. Sutures on the inner surface (endocranial) of the skull tend to incomplete closure, such incomplete closure is known as lapsed union. Suture closure is scored as 0 when there is no union, 1 when one-fourth of the suture has closed, 2 when one-half has closed, 3 when three-fourths of the suture is closed, and 4 when the suture is completely closed. There are no significant ethnic group or race differences in suture closure, though in prehistoric representatives of man the endocranial sutures tended to undergo closure at an earlier age.

A good rule to remember is that closure begins in S (sagittal) at 22 years, C (coronal) 24 years, L (lambdoid) 26 years; closure ends S 35 years, C 42 years, L 47 years. It is also well to remember that aging a skull by means of suture closure alone is a hazardous procedure, one may be as much as 20 years off in certain cases! Usually one can get within six years of actual age. Wherever feasible as many other characteristics as possible should be used in arriving at an estimate of age.

The Sex of the Skull

It is not possible with any degree of reliability to determine the sex of the skull until after puberty. In general the female skull is smaller and lighter than the male skull. It presents a more infantile appearance, the bones are smoother, more gracile, and more delicately fashioned. The supraorbital and temporal ridges are little if at all developed, the mastoid processes are small and the supramastoid crests scarcely developed, while the occipital muscle markings are weakly developed. The facial skeleton, teeth, mandible, zygomatic arches and cheekbones are smaller and more delicate, and the margins of the orbits are sharper in the female.[17]

Cranial Recording Blanks

Recording blanks for registering measurements and observations made on the skull will be found indispensable. A typical blank of this sort is reprinted here through the courtesy of Dr. J. L. Angel.

Cephalic and Cranial Deformation

Distorted or deformed crania are due to:

1. *Synostotic deformation:* consequent upon irregularities of cranial development, accompanied by precocious union of the cranial bones.

2. *Artificial deformation:* consequent upon pressure or compression applied during infancy.

3. *Pathological deformation:* the result of disease.

4. *Posthumous deformation:* consequent upon pressure exerted by the soil surrounding a skull.

The deformations considered:

1. *Synostotic deformation.* Synostosis of the cranial sutures may be either precocious or retarded. In premature synostosis, some deviation from the normal cranial form is very common, and a general rule (formulated by Rudolf Virchow) is that premature synostosis is followed by restricted growth in a direction perpendicular to that of the synostosed suture. Thus, if a longitudinally directed suture be closed by premature synostosis, the skull-growth in the transverse or coronal direction will be checked. Should the coronal suture or other trans-

---

[17] For the most recent study see Keen, J. A.: A study of the differences between male and female skulls. *Am. J. Phys. Anthropol.,* n.s. 8:65-78, 1950.

versely directed suture be obliterated, restriction of growth in the sagittal direction will ensue.

Forms of Synostotic Deformation

A. *Scaphocephaly:* Probably the commonest deformation associated with premature synostosis. There may be an appearance of annular constriction, and the specimens are always dolichocephalic, the narrowness being due to restricted growth transversely, in accordance with the law formulated above, following upon closure of the sagittal suture.

B. *Klinocephaly:* When the fore part of the sagittal suture is closed prematurely and at the same time the parieto-sphenoidal suture undergoes synostosis, the growth of the skull is arrested locally, at the sides and the top; this results in the production of a depression encircling the skull as though a band had been tightly applied.

C. *Trigonocephaly:* When the medio-frontal or metopic suture closes prematurely, localized arrest of transverse growth may follow; the frontal region will then remain narrow and stunted in growth, while the posterior parts of the cranium expand normally. The result is the production of a skull which, viewed from above, presents a perked or rostrated appearance, which has been described as triangular or trigonocephalic.

D. *Plagiocephaly:* The skull is asymmetrical. In typical cases there is closure of the coronal suture at a premature stage. The arrest in growth is then unilateral and the skull becomes flattened on one side, while in compensation the opposite side projects. Slight degrees of deformation of this kind may possibly be produced in childhood, if the infant lies habitually on one side rather than on the other.

E. *Acrocephaly:* The bones of the cranial vault are upraised, so that the height of the skull is much increased. These crania are usually very brachycephalic, and the coronal suture is often closed, while part of the sagittal suture near the bregma, and the basilar (basi-occipital) suture may partake in the synostotic processes.

Artificial Deformations

In artificial deformation of the head pressure is artificially applied in various ways and to various regions of the head.[18] The pressure may be:

    I. *Frontal:* Exercised by means of a board or other object against the forehead.

---

[18] A useful work is E. J. Dingwall, *Artificial Cranial Deformation.* London, John Bale, Sons & Danielsson, Ltd., 1931.

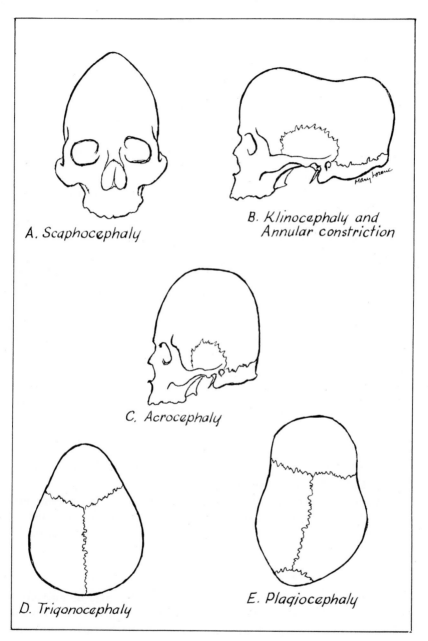

Figure 20. Types of cranial deformation.

II. *Fronto-Occipital* (Flat-head): Produced by means of pressure at the front and back of the head. There are bi-lobed and tri-lobed varieties, in which a rod is substituted for a flat surface, thus indenting the young head to which it is applied.

III. *Annular* (Aymara): Produced by tightly tying a bandage around the head.

IV. *Occipital:* Pressure applied to the back of the head.

V. *Plagiocephalic:* The compression is unequally exerted and the deformation is asymmetrical.

VI. *Platybasia:* The deformation in which the basis cranii appears to be thrust up into the cranial cavity.

Artificial cranial deformation does not affect the functioning of the brain in any way.

Pathological Deformation

I. *Hydrocephalus:* Excessive and even expansion of the constituents of the cranial walls. The sutures become separated as a result of the expansion leaving gaps which are rapidly filled by the formation of wormian bones, of which many scores may be present. The ventricles of the brain, and sometimes the subarachnoid spaces, are distended with fluid. The varieties of hydrocephalus have been classified according to the causes of the accumulation of the fluid.

II. *Microcephalus:* Premature arrest of the growth of the skull by early synostosis or union at sutures, with resulting diminutive size of skull.

III. *Rachitis* (or Rickets): The frontal bone is unusually prominent in its upper portion.

IV. *Sickle-Cell Anemia:* This disorder is associated with a remarkable bossing of the frontal bones.

V. Other bone diseases producing characteristic deformations are arthritis, acromegaly, congenital syphilis, leontiasis ossia, osteomalacia, Paget's disease, spondylitis deformans, and tuberculosis, being perhaps among the most important.

POSTCRANIAL OSTEOMETRY

The purposes for which the postcranial skeleton may be measured are varied. But whatever the purpose, measurements should always be adapted to throw the maximum light upon the problem under investigation. The investigator should always know *why* he is making

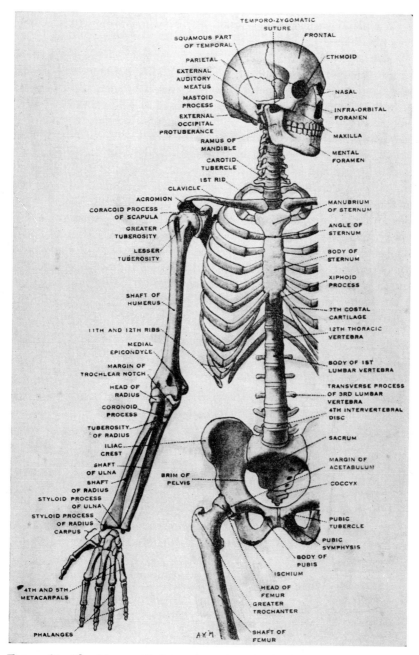

Figure 21. The Human Skeleton (anterior view). From Appleton *et al.* Courtesy, Williams & Wilkins.)

a particular measurement. Well constructed measurements can help to solve difficult problems.

Instruments. In addition to the instruments already described, larger versions of the sliding compass and spreading calipers are used, and the anthropometer sometimes used to serve the purposes of both, that is, as a rod compass and as a sliding caliper or pelvimeter. For the measurement of long bones an osteometric board is commonly used. The *osteometric board* is a flat, seasoned block of wood, some 23 inches long by 12 inches wide, and about one inch thick. Firmly and immovably attached to one end at an exact right angle is a wooden upright of some 8 inches. Inlaid or attached metric scales run the length of the board (preferably one on each side and one down the middle of the board). A free L-shaped wooden upright completes the instrument. To measure, one end of the bone is placed against the fixed upright and the movable upright against the other, so that the bone is enclosed between the two uprights. The length is then read off the scale at the edge of the movable upright. A satisfactory osteometric board can easily be made by using a 50 cm. square sheet of graduated millimeter graph paper.

Measurements

Upper Extremity and Scapula
Humerus, Radius and Ulna

1. *Maximum length* (osteometric board): Between the most proximal and most distal points, the bone being held parallel to the long axis of the board.

2. *Maximum diameter of head* (sliding compass).

3. *Antero-posterior middle shaft diameter* (sliding compass): At middle of shaft.

4. *Medio-lateral middle shaft diameter* (sliding compass): At middle of shaft.

5. *Maximum medio-lateral distal diameter* (sliding compass): At the epiphyseal end of the bone immediately above its associated processes.

6. *Radio-Humeral Index* $\dfrac{\text{Maximum Length Radius} \times 100}{\text{Maximum Length Humerus}}$

Scapula

7. *Morphological breadth* (sliding compass): From the highest point of the superior angle to the lowest point of the inferior angle.

8. *Morphological length* (spreading calipers): From the middle

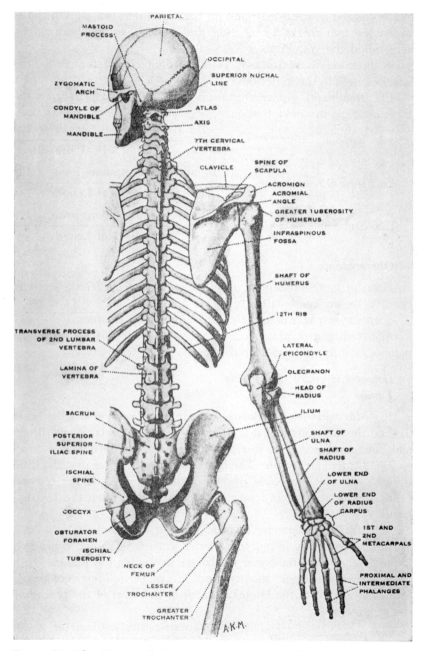

Figure 22. The Human skeleton (posterior view). (From Appleton *et al.* Courtesy, Williams & Wilkins.)

of the glenoid fossa to the point on the vertebral border midway between the two ridges terminating the scapular spine; this point is here called the vertebrion.

9. *Breadth of infraspinous fossa* (sliding compass): From the inferior angle to the vertebrion.

10. *Breadth of suprasinous fossa* (sliding compass): From the superior angle to the vertebrion.

11. *Scapular Index* $\dfrac{\text{Morphological Length} \times 100}{\text{Morphological Breadth}}$

12a. *Infraspinous Index* $\dfrac{\text{Breadth of infraspinous fossa} \times 100}{\text{Morphological Length}}$

12b. *Supraspinous Index* $\dfrac{\text{Breadth of supraspinous fossa} \times 100}{\text{Morphological Length}}$

Observations

Form of vertebral border, from superior angle: Convex, straight, concave, or any combination of these.

Scapular notch: Absent, slight, medium, deep, foramen.

Age changes: Lipping of margins of glenoid fossa, atrophic patches or rarefaction of scapular fossae.

Lower Extremity and Pelvis
Femur

13. *Maximum length:* Between the internal condyle and the head. To find this measurement it is necessary to move the bone slightly up and down and from side to side between the two uprights.

14. *Bicondylar length:* The two condyles rest up against the fixed upright and the moveable upright is brought against the femoral head, so that the whole femur rests naturally between the two uprights.

15. *Maximum diameter of head* (sliding compass).

16. *Subtrochanteric antero-posterior diameter* (sliding compass): Immediately below the lesser trochanter in the sagittal plane.

17. *Subtrochanteric medio-lateral diameter* (sliding compass): From the medial to the lateral surfaces at the level of the preceding measurements.

18. *Platymeric Index* $\dfrac{\text{Antero-posterior diameter} \times 100}{\text{Medio-lateral diameter}}$

Hyperplatymeric $\times$—74.9

Platymeric	75.0—84.9
Eurymeric	85.0—99.9
Stenomeric	100.0—×

The platymeric index may reflect and thus indicate differences in ethnic, occupational, pathological conditions, and also in such habits as sitting and squatting.

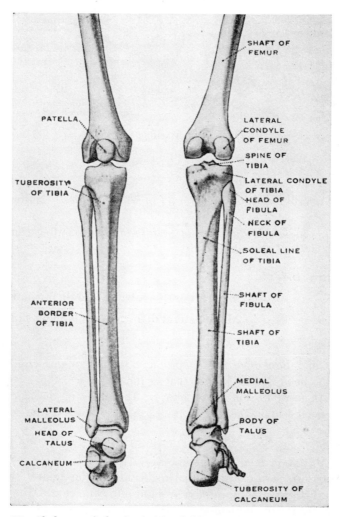

Figure 23. Skeleton of the leg. (On left) anterior aspect with bones of foot removed except talus and calcaneum; (on right) posterior aspect. (From Appleton *et al.* Courtesy, Williams & Wilkins.)

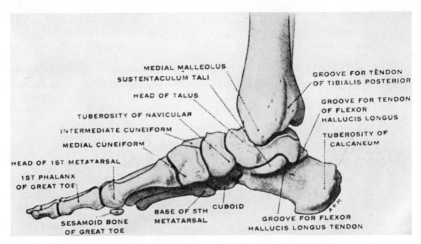

Figure 24. Skeleton of foot. Medial aspect. (From Appleton *et al.* Courtesy, Williams & Wilkins.)

19. *Antero-posterior diameter of middle of shaft* (sliding compass).

20. *Medio-lateral diameter of middle of shaft* (sliding compass): At same level as preceding.

Pilastric Index

$$\frac{\text{Antero-posterior diameter of middle of shaft} \times 100}{\text{Medio-lateral diameter of middle of shaft}}$$

Angles

21. *Collo-diaphyseal angle* (protactor): The angle made by the axis of the head and neck with that of the shaft.

22. *Angle of torsion* (protractor): The angle of the axis of the head projected upon the axis of the posterior surface of the condyles.

Tibia

23. *Maximum length* (osteometric board): The bone resting on its dorsal surface with the medial malleolus resting against the fixed upright. The movable upright is brought into contact with the antero-superior surface of the lateral condyle. The tibia must be parallel to the long axis of the board.

24. *Antero-posterior diameter middle of shaft* (sliding compass).

25. *Medio-lateral diameter of middle of shaft* (sliding compass).

26. *Antero-posterior nutrient foramen diameter* (sliding compass): Diameter of shaft at level of nutrient foramen.

27. *Medio-lateral nutrient foramen diameter* (sliding compass).

28. *Platycnemic Index* $\dfrac{\textbf{Medio-lateral nutrient diameter} \times \textbf{100}}{\textbf{Antero-posterior nutrient diameter}}$

Hyperplatycnemic	×—54.9
Platycnemic	55.0—62.9
Mesocnemic	63.0—69.9
Eurycnemic	70.0—×

Observations

Lateral condyle: Concave or convex.

Squatting facets: Note whether there are any extensions of the inferior articular surface above the anterior lip or medially at the distal end of tibia.

Vertebrae

29. *Anterior height of centrum* (sliding compass): From the middle of the antero-superior lip to the middle of the antero-inferior lip of the body.

30. *Posterior height of centrum* (sliding compass): From the middle of the postero-superior border to the middle of the postero-inferior border of the body.

Pelvis and Sacrum

31. *Maximum pelvic height* (rod compass): From the highest point on the iliac crest to the lowest point on the ischial tuberosity.

32. *Maximum pelvic or cristal breadth* (rod compass): Greatest diameter between the external lips of the right and left iliac crests.

33. *Pelvic Breadth-Height Index* $\dfrac{\textbf{Maximum Pelvic height} \times \textbf{100}}{\textbf{Maximum pelvic breadth}}$

34. *Interspinous diameter* (sliding compass): The maximum diameter between the antero-lateral margins of the antero-superior iliac spines.

35. *External Conjugate diameter* (pelvimeter): From the inferior tip of the 5th lumbar spine to the antero-inferior margin of the pubic symphysis.

36. *Diagonal conjugate diameter* (pelvimeter): From the mid-sagittal point on the antero-superior margin of the sacral promontory to the postero-inferior margin of the pubic symphysis.

37. *Normal conjugate diameter* (sliding compass): From the

postero-superior margin of the symphysis pubis to the deepest point
of the third sacral vertebra.

38. *Sagittal diameter of pelvic inlet* (sliding compass): From the
postero-superior border of the pubic symphysis to the center of the
sacral promontory.

39. *Transverse diameter of pelvic inlet* (sliding compass): Maximum diameter between arcuate lines.

40. *Pelvic Inlet Index*	$$\dfrac{\textbf{Sagittal diameter of pelvic inlet} \times \textbf{100}}{\textbf{Transverse diameter of pelvic inlet}}$$
Platypellic	×—89.9
Mesatipellic	90.0—94.9
Dolichopellic	95.0—×

In a study, by roentgen pelvimetry of 686 living white women,
and 107 girls from five to 15 years of age, Greulich and Thoms found
the following distribution of pelvic inlet indices:

	Platy-pellic per cent	*Mesati-pellic per cent*	*Doli-chopellic per cent*
582 primiparous clinic women (lower socio-economic classes)	35.2	27.5	37.3
104 nulliparous student nurses (higher socio-economic classes)	13.5	13.5	73.0
107 children	8.4	35.2	82.2

Of the 686 women studied 68.1 per cent had a pelvic inlet index
of 90 or more. Only 31.9 per cent were of the platypellic type which
the textbooks generally describe as typical.

In 69 male medical students at Yale the same authors found the
pelvic inlet index to vary between 77.0 to 121.0, with an average
index of 100.5. The frequencies were 7.2 per cent platypellic, 14.5
mesatipellic, and 78.2 dolichopellic.

41. *Inferior antero-posterior diameter* (sliding compass): From
the postero-inferior border of the pubic symphysis to the postero-
inferior border of the sacrum.

42. *Distance between ischial spines* (sliding compass): Minimum.

43. *Intertuberous diameter* (sliding compass): Minimum diameter between the postero-medial margins of the ischial tuberosities.

44. *True pelvic height* (sliding compass): From the lowest point
on the medial margin of the ischial tuberosity to the arcuate line
anterior to ileopectineal eminence.

Sacrum

45. *Anterior sacral length* (sliding compass): From the middle of sacral promontory to the middle of the antero-inferior margin of the last sacral vertebra.

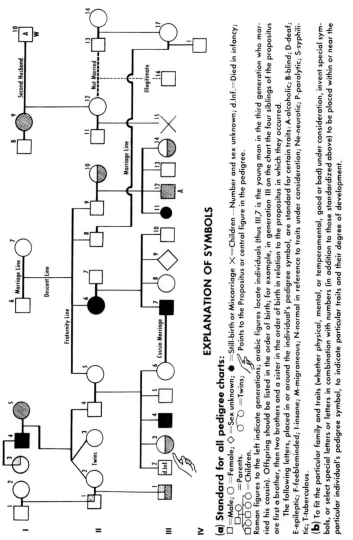

Figure 25. Sample genetic pedigree chart. (From Ashley Montagu. Courtesy, World Publishing Co.)

46. *Anterior sacral breadth* (sliding compass): At junction with arcuate lines.

47. *Length-Breadth Sacral Index* $\dfrac{\text{Anterior sacral breadth} \times 100}{\text{Anterior sacral length}}$

Dolichohieric	×— 99.9
Subplatyhieric	100.0—105.9
Platyhieric	106.0—×

Sexual Characters of the Pelvis

It is possible to determine the sex of the skeleton in a large percentage of cases from the characters of the pelvis. Variability is, however, very considerable. Each sex may exhibit the typical pelvic characters of the opposite sex. One can, therefore, never be quite certain that sex has been accurately determined from the characters of the pelvis. Below is given a list of 21 characters in which the female pelvis and sacrum generally differs from that of the male.

Pelvic Characters	In the Female
Cristal breadth	Less
Iliac crest	Less rugged
Tubercles of iliac crest	Much less marked
Anterior and posterior slopes iliac crest	Less steep
Iliac blades or bones	More vertical
Iliac part of ileopectineal line	Greater
Sagittal diameter of pelvic inlet	Greater
Transverse diameter of pelvic inlet	Greater
Symphysis pubis	Broader and lower
Symphyseal height	Less
Ischial portion of pubic bone	Lipped outward, constricted just below symphysis
Subpubic angle	Greater
Intertuberous breadth	Greater
Acetabulum	Lighter
Diameter between ischial spines	Greater
Greater sciatic notch	Broader and more shallow
Preauricular sulci or grooves	Present and well developed
Sacrum	Broader and shorter
Sacral curve	Less
Lower portion of sacrum	Bent backward and upward

Washburn has devised an ischium-pubis index which will accurately sex, according to him, over 90% of skeletons. Length of ischium is measured from the point at which ischium, pubic, and ilium meet in the acetabulum. In the adult this point can be approximately identified because: (1) there is often an irregularity present both in acetabulum and inside the pelvis, (2) holding the bone up to a light will reveal a change in thickness, and (3) there is frequently a notch in the border of the articular surface of the acetabulum. In making measurements hold calipers parallel to long axis of each bone. It is, of course, understood that sexing will be carried out on skeletons belonging to a single division of mankind. The pubic bone is absolutely and relatively larger in females than in males.

$$\frac{\text{Pubis Length} \times 100}{\text{Ischium Length}} = \text{Ischium-Pubis Index}$$

The ischium-pubis index averages 15% higher in females than in males. The mean index in white males was found to be 83.6 (range 73-94) ± 4.0, for white females 99.5 (range 91-115) ± 5.1. In Negro males the comparable figures were 79.9 (range 71-88) ± 4.0, and in Negro females 95.0 (range 84-106) ± 4.6. Only 5 white males were found to fall within the range of female variation. More overlapping occurs among Negroes, probably due to ethnic mixture.

PEDIGREES FOR GENETIC STUDIES

Figure 25 shows a sample pedigree chart together with an explanation of the symbols. For the traits listed any others may be substituted at the convenience of the investigator.

THE MEASUREMENT OF BODY COMPOSITION *

HISTORICAL PERSPECTIVE

TRADITIONALLY physical anthropologists have been interested in the skeleton. Osteometry covered a large part of the *globus anthropologicus.* Skeletal remains were plentiful and anthropologists were busy and happy. Insofar as measurements were involved, rather than qualitative descriptions and classifications of the color of skin, shape of the nose, or texture of the hair, anthropologists compared the living representatives of the races of mankind again in terms of skeletal dimensions. The techniques of physical anthropology were designed to render as negligible as possible the individual differences in fat and muscle.

The result was that anthropologists got, for the most part, what they asked for: data on the skeleton only.[1] Man, the professed subject matter of anthropology's inquiry, was squeezed out. The portion of the human body between the skin and the bone was a "no-man's-land," lying fallow. The realization was slow in coming that soft tissues *were* the anthropologist's business and that body composition is, in fact, the very key to human physique.

Body weight was measured, though more frequently by pediatricians, internists, including medical life-insurance examiners, and teachers than by those whose business was to study man's physique, *ex officio.* What has been wrong with body weight, anthropologically speaking, was the way it was used. As length determines in part body weight, a variety of height-weight indexes were devised. They had a common fault: at best, they yielded a gross measure of underweight-overweight, lumping together factors that should be kept initially apart.

In the adult individual, at a given height the body weight increases 1) with the increase in lateral dimensions of the skeletal frame; such an increase is accounted for, in a small measure, by the

---

* By Josef Brožek, Lehigh University, Bethlehem, Pennsylvania; Research Associate and formerly Professor, Laboratory of Physiological Hygiene, School of Public Health, University of Minnesota, Minneapolis, Minnesota.

weight of the "extra" skeletal structures and, more importantly, by increased amounts of the supporting musculature and by the increased size of the organs filling the spaces defined by the bony structures, 2) with increase in musculature, resulting from physical exercise, and with increase in adipose tissue, resulting from excessive food intake and/or underexercise.

These factors, of quite different biological significance, are hopelessly scrambled in height-weight indexes and allied concepts, such as the relative body weight (100 A/S, where A = actual weight, S = weight standard for age, sex and height). How can we partition the gross body weight?

The basic information regarding body composition is obtained on the basis of direct analysis of the human body. Because of man's size and a variety of other considerations, quantitative analyses of whole adult bodies using anatomical or chemical methods have been few and far between. There was a long gap between the work of the older German anatomists (Bischoff 1863, Volkmann 1874) and the modern data published in America by Mitchell (1945, 1953) and in England by McCance (1951) and their respective collaborators. Their work, though limited in the number and selection of the bodies, represents a significant advance. Clearly, the direct analyses provide the final calibration and validation for the indirect methods.

Individual differences in soft-tissues, specifically in subcutaneous fat, have not escaped the measurers' eyes. P. Richer, a Frenchman, reported on "the function of fat in the external form of the human body" as far back as 1890. But the roots of modern anthropological study of body composition, utilizing available anatomical information and focussed on the analysis of body weight based on external body measurements, may be traced to the work of the Czech anthropologist J. Matiegka. His important paper [2] was published in 1921 under the cryptic title "The testing of physical efficiency" in the *American Journal of Physical Anthropology*. Much interested in the functional significance of individual differences in human physique, Matiegka outlined a technique for a quantitative appraisal of the mass of the main body compartments accessible to somatometric approach. The writer has expressed the opinion, and still holds it, that it was a major loss for students of human physique that Matiegka's approach, providing physical anthropology with its vital "fourth dimension" remained, for years, unnoticed.

In subsequent years the studies of the composition of the human body continued to receive impetus through a variety of developments. At Minnesota R. E. Scammon, quantitatively oriented anatomist, portrayed in the early twenties the markedly varying rates at which different organs grow,[3] with special emphasis on the fetal period. The layer of subcutaneous fat grows precipitously between about the 28th and 40th week of menstrual age (term). Equations were provided for predicting from crown-heel length the weight of the anatomically separated subcutaneous adipose tissue and of the chemically extracted fat.[4]

R. E. Moulton, concerned with growth and development of farm animals, formulated in 1923 the concept of "chemical maturity," defined as a state in which the composition of the fat-free mass (analyzed in terms of water, protein, and minerals) approximates constancy.[5] While the species differences cannot be neglected, animal studies provide a welcome opportunity for the validation of indirect techniques.[5a]

Methodologically, an important advance in animal studies on body composition was made by J. Hammond. His complete-dissection method (1932) involves anatomical separation of the total body into its component organs and tissues. The weight of each component is recorded and expressed as percentage of total weight or, preferably, in terms of a reference organ or part (such as brain-plus-eyes). Hammond and his co-workers applied this technique to a systematic analysis of developmental changes in different anatomical regions and in the major organs and tissues of the body.[6]

The strongest stimulus to the study of body composition in man came from the work of A. R. Behnke, initially an outgrowth of his physiological studies pertaining to deep sea diving.[7, 8] Under his guidance formulae were developed for the analysis of weight of the living human body into its "fat" and "lean" fraction on the basis of the ratio of body weight to body volume[9] and of total body water.[10, 11]

In the context of nutritional researches Icie G. Macy and her co-workers began their studies on chemical growth during childhood. The first volume of their reports was published in 1942.[12] Later, they labelled the field "chemical anthropology." A large amount of valuable data was recorded and analyzed in regard to the storage of nutrients in the body of the growing child. Food intake was meticulously measured and the detailed chemical analysis of meals was combined with the collection and chemical analysis of excreta. The balance studies, involving determinations of the cumulative differences between nutrient intake and losses in urine and feces, were made for as long as 225 days—a truly Herculean labor! The metabolic balances provided detailed information on the storage of nitrogen, considered as evidence of the growth of "protoplasmic mass," and of minerals. A variety of anthropometric, physiological and other biochemical data were collected to document the complex changes constituting growth. The subsequent attempt to synthesize the simpler body measurements with the more complex biophysical and biochemical approaches to the analysis of body composition—an important task for physical anthropology—cannot be regarded as successful.[13, 13a]

The concepts and tools for the study of body composition were reviewed systematically in the comprehensive framework of human biology, as practiced at Minnesota.[14] The methodological contributions of the Minnesota group included some technical improvements (direct measurement of "residual air" in determinations of body volume by underwater weighing), the concept of normal young man as the "reference body," information on density of human fat and on the composition of mass gained by overeating ("obesity tissue"), and prediction of total fat from skinfolds and from roentgenograms of the extremities.

The technique of soft-tissue roentgenography has been utilized intensively for measuring the amounts of subcutaneous fat (plus skin), muscle and bone in several research centers concerned with growth and development.[15, 16, 17]

The concept of body composition, together with the availability of new tools for the measurement of body compartments, stimulated in recent years a substantial amount of research. Physical anthropology was brought into livelier contact with the "dynamic" problems of nutrition, of growth and aging, of physical exercise. The need for a fundamental rethinking of one of the pillars of physical anthropology of the living man, that of body build, emerged clearly.

METHODS—BASIC CONSIDERATIONS

The components into which the total body mass is separated depend on the investigator's frame of reference—anatomical, chemical, and biochemical (see Table III). The anatomist thinks in terms of dissected organs and tissues, of mechanically separable components that can be measured in regard to their size and weighed. The organic chemist, analyzing a whole cadaver or its anatomical parts, operates with compartments defined in terms of chemical procedures. And the biochemist and physiologist, dealing with a living organism will operate with a set of body components that will again differ, at least in part, from those of the organic chemist. The biochemical approach and breakdown of body weight is guided by metabolic and functional considerations, and results in a system in which some components are defined in strictly chemical terms (e.g., body water), others (e.g., cell mass) are "histochemical" constructs, i.e., tissue (*histos*) masses defined on the basis of biochemical operations and concepts.

The physical anthropologist is closer to the anatomist than to the chemist, whether he is making anthroposcopic ratings, using direct body measurements or measuring the width of tissues in a soft-tissue roentgenogram of the leg. His "fat" is the adipose tissue of the anatomist and his measurements of "muscles" or "bones" refer to anatomical entities. Yet, prediction equations can be established for the assessment of body composition, on the basis of appropriate body measurements, in terms of anatomically, chemically or biochemically defined components.

Prior to the discussion of individual methods, an overall review of the basic data used in studies of body composition *in vivo* may be useful. These are indicated in Table IV. A variety of other techniques was developed for the study of body composition, including determinations of body fat by the use of fat-soluble indicators, such as the gases nitrogen and cyclopropane, and the estimations of the fat-free fraction of the body from creatinine excretion and basal oxygen consumption. These methods will not be described here. The densitometric and the hydrometric method will be discussed only in regard to the basic ideas.

TABLE III

BASIC FRAMES OF REFERENCE AND THE RESULTING BODY COMPONENTS

Frames of Reference		
Anatomical	*Chemical* (Direct analysis of cadavers)	*Biochemical* (Indirect analysis *in vivo*)
Adipose tissue	Fat (ether extract)	Fat estimate (equivalent of ether extract)
	Total body water (by desiccation)	Total body water and its fractions (by dilution)
Muscle Mass, Viscera	Protein (6.25 × nitrogen)	Cell mass (estimate)
Skeletal mass	Total and bone mineral (ash)	Bone mineral (estimate)

TABLE IV

Basic Data Used in Different Approaches to Body Composition In Vivo

"Surface" Anthropometry	Roentgenogram-metry	Densitometry	Hydrometry
Height, Weight Relative Weight (Actual, as % of standard)	(Body weight)	Body weight	Body weight
Skinfolds	Width of skin plus subcutaneous tissues	Body density (D = Mass/Volume)	Total body water
Circumferences and diameters (especially in limbs, preferably corrected for subcutaneous fat)	Width of muscle layer (in limbs)	(Extracellular fluid)	Extracellular fluid
Bony diameters	Bony widths		
	(Degree of bone mineralization)		

The emphasis will be placed on those techniques that belong in the physical anthropologist's tool box. This is, however, a metaphor. It is easy enough to pack and carry around a box containing a couple of flexible steel tapes, a suitable L-shaped object for defining the level of the top of the head, large spreading calipers for measuring the width of shoulders and of the pelvis, smaller spreading calipers for determination of biepicondylar diameters of the extremities, and skinfold calipers. The x-ray machine is less readily transportable. Yet, in the last two decades soft-tissue roentgenography has been an important tool allowing the anthropologist to make a significant contribution to the fund of knowledge on the body composition of the living man. This tool has been applied especially to the study of growth and development while the densitometric technique was applied almost solely and the hydrometric technique largely to adults. In this presentation, we shall be also concerned primarily with the adult man (and, on occasion, the adult woman). Methods for research on growth were described recently by Garn and Shamir.[18]

METHODS: DISSECTION AND CHEMICAL ANALYSIS

For well over 100 years parts of dissected human bodies have been diligently weighed and some analyzed chemically. Nevertheless, information on the total composition of the body, in anatomical or chemical terms, is surprisingly meager. Most of the modern data were obtained since 1945.

The data resulting from the dissection of two cadavers into the various organs and tissues are given in Table V. The 35-year-old man died from a heart attack.[19] The death of the 46-year-old man was due to a skull fracture as a result of a fall.[20] Both were thin, below standard weight (with relative weights of 88 and 74, respectively; "normal" = 100). The authors reported the weights for 18 components. For our purposes the separation of body weight into that of skeleton, skin, adipose tissue, striated muscles, and a remainder will suffice.

For the purposes of integrating the direct analyses with the in-direct methods applicable to the living man it is essential to charac-terize the composition of the body in chemical terms. Some very detailed chemical analyses have been reported.[21] The best available data regarding moisture (total water), total fat (ether extract), pro-tein (6.25 × nitrogen), and ash (bone mineral plus non-osseous body minerals) are summarized in Table VI.

We are far from having satisfactory information in regard to the variations in body composition within the range of "normality," asso-ciated with such basic biological variables as age and sex.

METHODS: BODY MEASUREMENTS (SOMATOMETRY)

How do the traditional body measurements fit into the conceptual framework of body composition? The fact is that most of them do not fit it or at least do not fit it very effectively. The classical handbooks are brief or silent on the subject.[22]

Here we shall consider

a) linear measures of the development of subcutaneous adipose tissue and of muscularity, and
b) deviations of body weight from the "norm,"
c) estimation of principal tissue masses from body measurements.

TABLE V

ANATOMICAL BODY COMPOSITION OF BODIES OF 2 WHITE MEN [19,20]

Age, years	35	46
	Weights as % of total body weight	
Skeleton	14.8	17.6
Skin	7.8	6.3
Adipose tissue	13.6	11.4
Striated muscle	31.6	39.8
Remainder	32.2	24.9

TABLE VI

Body Composition Resulting from Chemical Analysis

Reference	(21)	(19)	(21)	(20)
Age, years	42	35	25	46
Sex	F	M	M	M
Weight, kg.	45.1	70.6	71.8	55.7

Weight of Components Expressed as % of Total Body Weight

Fat	23.6	12.5	14.9	19.7
Water	56.0	67.9	61.8	55.7
Protein	14.4	14.4	16.6	18.8
Ash	5.8	4.8	6.4	5.5
Unaccounted for	0.2	0.4	0.3	0.3

Weight of Components Expressed as % of Fat-free Body Weight

Water	73.3	77.6	72.6	69.3
Protein	18.8	16.5	19.5	23.4
Ash	7.6	5.5	7.5	6.8
Unaccounted for	0.3	0.4	0.4	0.5

Linear Measures of Fatness and Muscularity

Skinfolds

In man about one-half of the total fat deposits is present as the subcutaneous adipose tissue. In various parts of the body surface the skin, together with the subcutaneous layer, can be readily lifted ("folded"). As the thickness of the skin itself is relatively uniform, the differences in the thickness of the skinfolds measured at different *sites* in a given individual or at a given site in different *individuals*, reflect largely the differences in the amount of subcutaneous fat.

The number of sites at which skinfold measurements can be made is large. The number and location of sites that should actually be measured will depend on the investigator's aim and circumstances under which the measurements are to be done.

Over the last dozen years several skinfold calipers have been designed.[23] A model developed by Doctor K. O. Lange, in consultation with the present writer, is pictured in Figure 26. It is fortunate that, in spite of the existing differences in construction, the caliper pressure at the contact surfaces was kept at the standard value of 10 gm/mm². The contact area should be small so that it remains in full contact with the skin and the caliper pressure is well defined. Depending somewhat on the shape (circular, square, rectangular), the recommended size of the contact surfaces lies roughly between 20 and 40 mm².

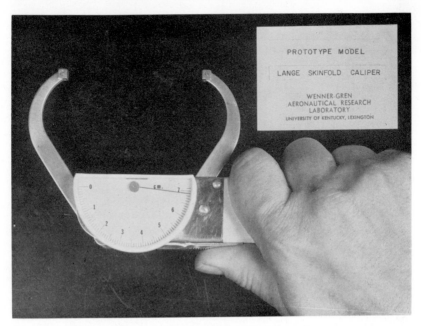

Figure 26. Lange Skinfold Caliper.*

Several other features must be standardized in order to assure comparability of skinfold measurements made by different investigators. Thus the "skin" should be lifted by grasping firmly the fold between the thumb and the forefinger. A firm grip, not exceeding the pain threshold, eliminates or at least substantially reduces the variations in the apparent thickness of skinfold that would result from wide differences in the pulling force of the fingers.

The width of the skin that is enclosed between the fingers is an important factor. It cannot be standardized, in its absolute size, for all the sites of the body. With a thick subcutaneous layer a wider segment of the skin must be "pinched" in order to form a fold than when the adipose tissue is poorly developed, as it is on the dorsum of the hand. For a given site the width of the skin should be *minimal,* still yielding a well defined fold.

The depth of the skinfold at which the calipers are placed on the fold also requires comment. The two sides of the fold are not likely to be parallel, when the skin is lifted by one hand, being narrower near the crest and larger toward the base. When the calipers are

* Available from the Wenner-Gren Aeronautical Research Laboratory, University of Kentucky, Lexington, Kentucky.

placed at the base, the resulting measurement is too large. Here, again, the correct distance from the crest is defined as the *minimal* distance from the crest at which a true fold, with surfaces approximately parallel to each other and to the contact surfaces of the calipers, is obtained upon the application of the calipers to the skin.

Some caliper models only approximate but do not actually achieve the parallelism of the contact surfaces. However, such parallelism is a desirable feature of the calipers. In very obese individuals at some sites no true skinfolds, as defined above, can be obtained. The measurements are still useful as indicators of fatness but the "skinfold" measurements are then larger than a double value of skin plus the subcutaneous layer, taking into account the compression of the tissues by the calipers. It is recommended to lift the skinfold at a distance of about 1 cm. from the site at which the calipers are to be placed and the skinfold measured.

Because of fairly rapid changes in the layer of the subcutaneous fat over relatively small distances at certain areas of the body surface, the sites should be clearly defined and carefully identified prior to measuring skinfolds in a given individual.

The selection of the location of the sites depends on several criteria, such as accessibility, the precision with which the location can be identified and reproduced, relative homogeneity of the layer of subcutaneous fat in a given region, and the validity of skinfold measurements at specified sites as an index of total body fat.

Taking into consideration all these criteria, clearcut superiority cannot be claimed for any one site. At present there is a fairly unanimous agreement on two sites which should be included in the minimum battery of somatic measurements gathered for purposes of anthropometric characterization of body composition: the dorsal skinfold on the upper-arm and the subscapular skinfold.[24]

The upper-arm site is readily accessible in individuals of both sexes in most cultures. The skinfold is located on the dorsum of the right upper-arm (over the triceps), at the level midway between the lateral margin of the acromial process of the scapula and the tip of the elbow. The level is located with the arm flexed at 90°. In making the skinfold measurement, the arm should hang freely. The crest of the skinfold is parallel to the long axis of the arm. As the changes in the thickness of subcutaneous fat from the elbow toward the shoulder are substantial, the level at which the skinfold is measured should be located rather precisely.

The subscapular skinfold is measured below the tip of the right scapula, with the subject standing but relaxed. Usually the skin is lifted most readily along a line at about 45° from the horizontal level, going medially upward (and laterally downward). One of the advantages of this site is that the thickness of the subcutaneous adipose layer is fairly homogeneous in this area and small differences in locating the site are less important than is true for the upper arm or the abdomen and chest.

A variety of other sites have been examined. The site along the mid-axillary line, at the level of the xiphoid process, appears advantageous as a predictor of total body fat.

When it is desirable to combine several skinfolds, 3 procedures can be used: 1) the skinfold thicknesses may be simply added—a least satisfactory method which is, nevertheless, justified for some purposes; 2) a measure of the "general fat-factor" may be derived on the basis of the statistical analysis of relations between the skinfolds, and 3) the skinfolds can be combined in a multivariate estimating equation so as to predict most effectively the total body fat, obtained by the densitometric or the hydrometric methods.

Limb Diameters (Muscle and Bone)

In the general population the differences in muscular development account for a lesser portion of variation in total body weight, at a given height, than does the size of the fat deposits. Nevertheless, quantitative characterization of musculature is of interest, especially to physical anthropologists concerned with the effects of exercise and physical work on man's physique.

Unfortunately, only the musculature of the extremities is readily accessible to anthropometric appraisal. When the required equipment and trained personnel are available, the size of the muscles can best be characterized in terms of the breadths (or calculated cross-sectional surfaces) of the muscular segments on the soft-tissue roentgenograms of the limbs. This method is referred to later in the text. When direct (somatometric) measurements must be relied upon, the muscular development of an individual can be characterized on the basis of limb circumferences, provided the thickness of the subcutaneous fat is measured at the same level as the limb circumference.

For the purposes of calculation, the limb is regarded as a cylinder. From the circumference (c), which is measured, we can calculate the total diameter ($c = \pi$ d; $d = c/\pi$). The corrected diameter is obtained by subtracting the thickness of skin-plus-subcutaneous layer. On the upper arm one may measure the dorsal (S_1, over triceps) and ventral (S_2, over biceps) skinfold and use these figures for correction of the total diameter. As the skinfolds represent 2 thicknesses of the adipose layer, only one-half of the skinfold thickness is subtracted:

$$d = c/\pi - \frac{S_1}{2} - \frac{S_2}{2}$$

In practice one usually measures only the dorsal skinfold and obtains the corrected diameter as

$$d = c/\pi - S_1$$

The upper arm circumference should be taken with the arm hanging freely. It should be measured at a right angle to the long axis of the arm, at the same level as the arm skinfold (midway between acromion and the olecranon, as indicated above). The flexible steel tape should be applied lightly to the skin in order to avoid deforming the contour of the skin.[24]

The calculated calf diameter is a useful indicator of the muscular development of the lower extremities. The circumference is measured at the level of the maximal cross-sectional area, preferably with the leg placed on a chair and bent at a 90° angle. Medial skinfold is used for purposes of correction.

A more "dynamic" measure of muscularity is represented by the circumference of the upper arm, flexed under tension in order to produce maximal bulging of the triceps.

Deviations from Standard Weight

Weight Predicted from Height

The deviation of body weight from the "standard" for height (and sex and age) may serve as a gross indicator of under- or overdevelopment of soft tissues (adipose tissue, musculature, and viscera). In pathological situations other body components, such as the body fluids accumulated in patients with "hunger edema," can complicate the interpretation of the biological significance of deviations from standard in such a manner as to make body weight useless even as a very gross indicator of soft-tissue development.

Athletes performing certain types of physical exercise, notably weight-lifting, develop large muscles. In such cases the muscle mass will account for a larger fraction of body weight than would be true for the average man. In "normal" adults of a given height the adipose tissue accounts for a large fraction of the individual differences in body weight.

The standard weight is usually defined as the average weight of individuals of a given sex, height, and age. In the United States the basic tables of standard weights are those developed in the course of medico-actuarial investigations.[23a] These tables were reprinted many times, with or without essentially arbitrary corrections for the height of shoes and the weight of shoes and clothes worn by the life insurance applicants on whom the data were based.

When the number of persons measured is very large, the standard weights can be obtained by averaging the weights of men and of women of a given age and height and tabulating them, separately for the two sexes. Even then some "smoothing" of the curves portraying the age trends is usually desirable, especially for the very tall and very short individuals who are in short supply.

For a given age we can calculate the predicted weight (the "standard") from a linear equation

$$S = a + bH$$

where a is an absolute value (a weight, in kg. or lb.), b is a regression coefficient (a number), and H is standing height (in cm. or in in.).

When a more general prediction equation is desired, the age factor (Y, in years) may be included. Then the equation assumes the form

$$S = a + b_1H + b_2Y$$

In order to compare different individuals, the deviation of the actual weight (A) from the standard (S), d = A-S, may be related to the standard weight:

$$d\% = 100\,\frac{A\text{-}S}{S}$$

More frequently, the Relative Weight is computed by relating not the deviation but the actual weight to the standard

$$\text{Relative Weight} = 100\,\frac{A}{S}$$

In the population of the U.S. the weight of adults tends to increase during the period of maturity and the tables of standard weights take this fact into account. Thus the relative weight of individuals of average weight (for height, sex and age), at all ages, is 100. These are the so-called age-corrected standards. They are useful for some comparisons of individuals differing in age. Specifically, they allow us to identify groups of individuals of different ages but of the same degree of relative underweight or overweight.

From the point of view of body composition studies, the use of a single standard, such as the average weight of individuals 25 years of age, of a given sex and height, makes good sense. Deviations from such a standard provide a better estimate of leanness-fatness while the relative weight is an appropriate measure of underweight-over-weight. It is essential to specify which standard is being used in a given study and to interpret the deviations from the standard accordingly.

From the statistical point of view the severe limitation of height-weight tables lies in the fact that the frequency of occurrence of a given value of relative body weight is not given. How many individuals have a Relative Weight greater than 110 or smaller than 90? This information is important for the appraisal of the biological significance of the weight deviations from standard.

The weight distributions are typically skewed toward the higher values. Consequently, the arithmetical averages (means) are larger than the "typical," most frequent values (mode) or the mid-points of the weight distributions (median, a value dividing the distribution into two equal halves). For some purposes attempts to remove the non-normality of the weight distributions by means of transformation (e.g. by using logarithms of body weights rather than the weights themselves) may be called for.

Weight Standards Taking Into Account Skeletal Frame and Muscularity

In the common height-weight standards only the height (and age) is taken into account as the point of reference: the variations in "body build" are not considered. The vertical partitioning of the body into head plus trunk versus the leg length appear to be less relevant than the consideration of the lateral bony dimensions. The measures of laterality should not be affected by the overlaying adipose tissue (or musculature). The Committee on Nutritional Anthropometry (1956) recommended two measures as indicators of the laterality of the skeletal frame: 1) the bicristal (biiliac) and 2) the biacromial diameter.[24]

The bicristal diameter, a measure of the width of the pelvic girdle, is obtained as the greatest distance between the lateral margins of the iliac crests. In well "padded" individuals it is necessary to exert strong pressure on the contact surfaces of the calipers in order to minimize the amount of soft tissues which would be otherwise included in this measurement. The failure to do so would result in a spuriously large "standard" weight, in the calculation of which the two diameters (and height) are included, and thus an underestimate of relative weight.

The biacromial diameter, a measure of the width of the shoulder girdle, is defined as the distance between the most lateral margins of the acromial processes of the scapulae. The subjects should stand erect but with the shoulders relaxed. This point is important and the failure to standardize the posture so as to obtain the maximal value, for a given individual, will introduce sizable errors.

When we wish to obtain a purer estimate of fatness, we should incorporate one or more criteria of muscular development into the prediction equation. The upper arm diameter, corrected for the thickness of the layer of subcutaneous fat may serve as such a criterion.

An equation for estimating "standard" weight on the basis of 5 predictors is given, as an example, in Table VII. The equation was derived on the basis of data obtained for 238 Minneapolis firemen.[25]

On the basis of statistical tests, 2 additional dimensions used initially as predictors of weight were eliminated: the iliocristal height, a measure of "leg length," and the biepicondylar diameter of the humerus, a measure of the "ruggedness" of the bones of the extremities. Each of the remaining 5 variables contributes significantly to the precision with which we can predict the body weight.

Deviations from a weight standard so defined may be interpreted as representing largely the amounts of adipose tissue by which an individual differs from the average man of given body proportions (and age).

TABLE VII

Equation for Predicting Body Weight ($\hat{Y}$) from Height (X_1), 2 Measures of Laterality (Bicristal Diameter, X_2, and Biacromial Diameter, X_3), an Indicator of Muscular Development (Upper Arm Diameter, Corrected for Subcutaneous Fat, X_4) and Age (X_5). All Measurements are in cm., Age in Years

$$\hat{Y} = +0.411\ X_1$$
$$+1.204\ X_2$$
$$+0.885\ X_3$$
$$+7.342\ X_4$$
$$+0.220\ X_5$$
$$-135.510$$

Anatomical Body Compartments Predicted from Body Measurements

In 1921, J. Matiegka proposed an original and potentially useful system for the estimation of certain tissue masses on the basis of body measurements.[2] He felt, with justification, that traditional anthropometry did not yield a satisfactory description of human physique. Clearly, it would be erroneous to assign too great an importance to any single body dimension as an indicator of "fitness." Thus tallness, as judged by stature, is not necessarily an indication of overall physical superiority as it may be associated with a poorly developed musculature. Similarly, large body weight may indicate an unhealthy obesity rather than a powerful physique. The traditional combinations of two or more anthropometric dimensions in the form of an index also did not yield the answer, the principal reason being that the initial measurements, such as body weight or chest circumference, were complex data in which size and tissue composition were hopelessly scrambled.

Matiegka was interested in a functionally oriented, "dynamic" anthropometry and his goal was to devise a system for an analytical, quantitative description of human physique, a system that would be adequate for the evaluation of the somatic facet of fitness ("physical efficiency") for purposes of vocational guidance, choice of athletic pursuits or life insurance examinations. He was anxious to place physical anthropology of the living man into a wider framework of human biology and visualized the somatometric evaluation of physique as a component of a broader study of man's health and work capacity. Such a comprehensive evaluation would include, in addition to body measurements, a general clinical examination, physiological assessment of principal body functions, and the psychological (psychometric) evaluation of an individual. In fact the term "somatotechnic" methods appealed to him as a parallel to the "psychotechnic" procedures of applied psychology. His goal was to enhance the biological significance of body measurements and to increase the utility of physical anthropology, measured in terms of medical and social criteria.

In Matiegka's system the gross body weight (w) was divided into four components:

$$w = O + D + M + R$$

where O = the weight of the skeleton (*"ossa,"* bones),

      D = skin (*"derma"*) plus subcutaneous adipose tissue

$M = $ skeletal muscles, and

$R = $ remainder.

The first three components, defined in terms of anatomical entities, can be estimated on the basis of body measurement (Table VIII).

The estimation equations were derived on the basis of the author's experience and such data as were available in the literature, and were regarded by the author simply as first approximations. He was aware of the tentative nature and deficiencies of his approach, and in the original communication (1921) he pointed out several times the need for empirical validation and refinement. Refinement and better standardization was called for in regard to some of the basic measurements. Thus skinfolds were measured with a sliding compass with blunt points exerting only a mild pressure so that the skinfold would slip out of the branches of the calipers when not held by the fingers. This is not a very precise definition of pressure and the use of calipers with a constant tension is preferable.

While Matiegka was concerned with strengthening the practical usefulness of anthropological measurements, his ideas were of fundamental importance for quantitative human morphology in that he

TABLE VIII

Matiegka's Formulae for the Calculation of the Weight, in Grams, of the Skeleton (O), Skin Plus Subcutaneous Adipose Tissue (D) and Muscles (M)

$$O = o^2 \times L \times k_1 \qquad D = d \times S \times k_2 \qquad M = r^2 \times L \times k_3$$

where $k_1 = 1.2$, $k_2 = 0.13$, and $k_3 = 6.5$,

$L = $ stature, in cm., $S = $ body surface, in cm.^{2}

$$o = \frac{o_1 + o_2 + o_3 + o_4}{4}$$, with o_1 to o_4 representing the maximum transverse diameters of humeral and femoral condyles, wrist and ankle, in cm.

$$d = 1/2 \frac{d_1 + d_2 \ldots + d_6}{6}$$, with d_1 to d_6 referring to the thickness of the skinfold at the following sites: upper arm, above the biceps; the forearm, plantar side at maximum breadth; thigh, above quadriceps muscle, halfway between inguinal fold and the knee; calf of the leg; thorax, on costal margin, halfway between mammae and the umbilicus; and abdomen, halfway between the navel and the anterior superior iliac spine.

$$r = \frac{r_1 + r_2 + r_3 + r_4}{4}$$, with r_1 to r_4 representing the radii calculated from the circumferences of the arm, flexed, measured above the belly of the biceps; forearm, maximum; thigh, halfway between the trochanter and the lateral epicondyle; and leg, maximum circumference of the calf. The values were corrected for thickness of the subcutaneous tissue plus the skin.

pointed to a new way for the synthesis of individual body measurements in a meaningful biological frame of reference and emphasized the fundamental role of body composition in describing man's physique.

Quantitatively oriented anatomists and physical anthropologists, in and out of his native Bohemia, owe Matiegka a debt of hard labor, still largely unpaid. Additional research is needed in order to replace Matiegka's approximative constants by rigorously derived estimation equations, especially for the total amounts of muscle in the body. Matiegka's ideas for the estimation of the weight of the skeleton on the basis of stature and transverse bony diameters of the extremities were taken up, tested, and further developed by Mildred Trotter and her co-workers in the Department of Anatomy, Washington University, St. Louis, Missouri.[26] The diameters recommended by Matiegka for the living were measured on skeletons (not on cadavers) and the weight of each skeleton was estimated according to Matiegka's formula. This estimate was not more precise, unfortunately, than the estimate that could be obtained from stature alone. Better results could have been, perhaps, obtained by using the bony measurements and height as predictors in a multivariate estimating equation.

The following additional variables were measured for the femur: weight, length, and area of photographic projection of the total femur. The middle half of each femur was x-rayed and the area of the shadows corresponding to the compact bone was determined with the planimeter. The area of compact bone proved to be the best single predictor of skeletal weight. This is important as the value can be obtained also for the living man. Adding stature to compact-bone area improved substantially the precision of predicting total skeletal weight but the addition of transverse diameters did not yield a further gain in the precision with which the weight of the skeleton could be predicted. In the final report 5 variables (stature, femur, length, area of shaft, area of compact bone, and age) were related to skeleton on weight.[26a]

METHODS: SOFT-TISSUE ROENTGENOGRAPHY

Light roentgenograms of the extremities, obtained with appropriate combinations of exposure time and peak voltage,* provide useful means for measuring the relative amounts of bone, muscle, and skin-plus-subcutaneous adipose tissue. The need for precise, standardized

---

* Garn specifies 10 to 20 milliampere seconds and peak voltages varying from 35 to 75 kilovolts, depending on the thickness of the part to be x-rayed [18, p. 66].

positioning can hardly be overemphasized. The distance between x-ray tube and film should be large (6 ft.) so as to minimize the distortion due to the fact that the x-rays are not strictly parallel. J. M. Tanner eliminates the differences in the magnification effect present in x-raying parts that vary in thickness by keeping constant the distance between the medial plane of the limb and the film (see also [26b]).

For purposes of examining the relations of roentgenographic limb measurements to body density, roentgenograms were obtained of the upper arm and forearm, of thigh and leg.[27] The technique of measuring soft-tissue roentgenograms is illustrated in Figure 2. Three sites are presented: 1) Upper arm, in anteroposterior projection; of special interest is the thickness of subcutaneous fat, measured at the point of deltoid indentation along the line vertical to the skin (see also [28]). 2) Leg, in anteroposterior projection. All measurements were taken perpendicularly to the long axis of the limb, defined as the line connecting the midpoints of the upper and lower edges of the section of the limb, at the level of maximal width. 3) Mid-upper arm, in mediolateral projection, at a level half-way between acromion and olecranon; the measurements of the adipose and muscle layers were made along the line perpendicular to the long axis of the limb. The bone width was measured perpendicularly to the long axis of the bone.

The measurements were taken with a micrometer provided with sharp points and reading to 0.1 mm. In addition to linear measurements, the projected areas corresponding to the different tissues have been determined by some authors and cross-sectional areas of "fat," muscle and bone were calculated.

The x-ray technique is especially useful for determining the thickness of subcutaneous fat in those areas in which skinfolds cannot be measured and which exhibit, at the same time, marked individual differences. Garn's iliac and mid-trochanteric sites are outstanding examples of such sites ([18, p. 66]). On the leg only the medial skinfold can be readily measured, and only in men.

DENSITOMETRY

In a physical system consisting of two components (M_1, M_2) of known densities (d_1, d_2), determination of the density of the system (D) allows the calculation of the proportional masses of the 2 components (m_1, m_2; $m_1 + m_2 = 1$). The general formula may be written as follows:

$$m_1 = \frac{1}{D} \frac{d_1 \times d_2}{(d_2 - d_1)} - \frac{d_1}{(d_2 - 1)}$$

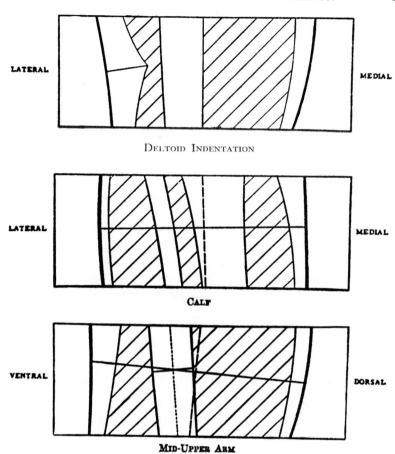

Figure 27. Illustrative examples of measurements made on soft-tissue roentgenograms. Next to the skin is the white area of subcutaneous fat. Shaded areas indicate muscles, the white areas between the muscular layers represent bones. Limb axes are indicated by long dashes, bone axis of the mid-upper arm by short dashes. The lines along which the measurements are made are solid.

where m_1 is the mass of the first component (M_1) expressed as a fraction of the total body mass, M; $m_1 = M_1/M$. The body volume, needed in calculations of body density (D = Mass/Volume) can be determined by underwater weighing, making correction for the air remaining in the lungs and respiratory passages,[29] or on the principle of inert-gas (helium) dilution.[30] But what are the two components, M_1 and M_2, into which the body can be divided?

In the Minnesota system [14] these two components are 1) the body of a "reference man" (R) defined as a 25-year old individual whose actual weight is identical with the tabular standard and whose intensity was determined empirically as $d_R = 1.0629$ gm./cc.[31] and 2) the tissue gained (G) as a result of simple overeating for a period of six months, with a $d_G = 0.948$.[32]

Using these densities in the general densitometric equation, we can calculate the amount (as fraction of body weight) of tissue similar to "G" that is present in an individual for whom the density was determined:

$$g = \frac{1}{D}8.753 - 8.235$$

"G" is not a pure fat, as defined chemically (having a density of 0.9007; [32a]), but an equivalent of a generalized adipose ("obesity") tissue. It was estimated that fat constitutes only about 62 per cent of the total weight gain. The fat by which a given individual differs from the reference man (ΔF; $\Delta F = 0.62G$) can be calculated from the formula

$$\triangle f = \frac{1}{D}5.427 - 5.106$$

For some purposes we wish to estimate not only the difference from the reference body but the total fat. Assuming that the body of the reference man contains 14 per cent of "fat" (as ether extract), the amount of total fat in a given body can be calculated, as fraction of body weight, as follows:

$$f = \frac{1}{D}4.201 - 3.813$$

The derivations of the formulae have been presented in detail.[14, 33] Behnke [34] operates with the concept of the "fat-free body" ($d = 1.0939$) and uses the value of 0.9018 as the density of fat. For these quantitative assumptions

$$f = \frac{1}{D}5.135 - 4.694$$

METHODS—HYDROMETRY

Clearly, the technical complexities of determining total body water and separating it into two fractions, the extracellular and intracellular, are beyond the level of an introductory presentation. Yet, the basic ideas and facts are simple.

The water "spaces" are measured on the principle of dilution. Various substances have been used for determination of total body water (antipyrine, urea, heavy water—deuterium, water labelled with radioactive hydrogen—tritium) and of its extracellular component (thiocyanate, correcting the resulting space by a factor of 0.7 to obtain the "true" extracellular space). The intracellular water is computed by difference, Total-Extracellular. Advances in methods make it possible to administer orally a test solute (tritium) for the determination of total body water and to use urine rather than blood serum as a sample of body fluids in which the substance was dissolved. This makes the hydrometric analysis of body composition more applicable to problems in which the physical anthropologist, working as a member of a research team, is likely to be interested.

In the first approximation, the body mass (M) can be considered as a two-component system:

$$M = F + N,$$

where F = fat, N = non-fat. Regarding the N-component as a body mass of relatively constant composition, we can calculate its amount knowing the fraction (c) of the non-fat portion of the body accounted for by water and having determined the total body water (T) of a given body. Then

$$T = cN, \text{ and}$$

$$N = \frac{T}{c}$$

Denoting the reciprocal of c, $\frac{1}{c} = k$, we may write $N = kT$.

Fat is derived by difference, $F = M - N$.

Expressing both components as fractions of body weight ($f + n = 1$) and using the value of the non-fat component calculated from total body water, we obtain

$$f = 1 - kt$$

The values of c as applied to adult man by various authors varied between 0.71 and 0.73, yielding k values of 1.41 and 1.37, respectively.

In a more comprehensive system, involving a larger number of numerical assumptions, the total body mass (M) may be separated into fat (F), water (T), and two types of non-fat solids: the dry cell residue (S) and the bone minerals (B)

With M = 1,
$$M = F + T + S + B$$
$$f = 1 - t - s - b$$

In addition to total body water (T), the extracellular water (E) is determined, and I, the intracellular water computed (I = T − E). The values of the bone minerals (B) and the non-fat non-water component of the cells (S) are estimated, using the intracellular water—a measure of the cell mass—as the reference point: $S = k_1 I$; $B = k_2 I$. In the Minnesota system [14, p. 290] the constants were estimated as $k_1 = 0.429$, $k_2 = 0.134$.

With I = T − E,
$$f = 1 - t - 0.429 \, (t-e) - 0.134 \, (t-e), \text{ so that in a}$$
simplified form, $f = 1 - 1.563t + 0.563e$

where t = total body water and e = extracellular fluid, both being expressed as fractions of body weight:

$$t = \frac{T}{M}, \quad e = \frac{E}{M}$$

METHODS: PREDICTION OF TOTAL BODY FAT FROM ANTHROPOMETRIC DATA

The linear somatic and roentgenographic measurements or areas and volumes calculated from them yield only a relative degree of leanness-fatness of a given individual. For some purposes we may wish to know the total amount of fat. This can be done, within the limits of uncertainties inherent in the underlying assumptions (and in methods of measurement), by relating the anthropometric data to the total body fat. This independent criterion can be provided by the densitometric or the hydrometric method. As the numerical interpretations of body density are open to modification, it is preferable to establish the equations for predicting density and only in the last step to convert the density values into "total fat."

Skinfolds as Predictors of Density

Equations have been provided, for young and middle-aged men, with skinfold measurements as predictors and body density as criterion of leanness-fatness.[35] The study was repeated for young men [36] taking into account subsequent refinements in techniques for measuring both skinfold thicknesses and body density. Skinfold measurements were made at a variety of sites. Body volume, used for calculation of body density, was determined by underwater weighing. Using only those skinfolds which contributed significantly to the efficiency of prediction, the following multiple regression equation was derived:

$$\hat{Y} = 1.088468 - .0007123X_1 - .0004832X_2 - .0005513X_3$$

where $\hat{Y}$ is the estimated body density (to be converted into the fat content of the body), X are the skinfold thicknesses in millimeters taken, respectively, at the chest in the midaxillary line at the level of the xiphoid (X_1), at the chest in the juxta-nipple position (X_2), and on the dorsum of the upper arm at the midpoint between the acromion and the olecranon. The values of density should be rounded, following the arithmetical manipulations, to 3 decimal places. Prediction equations based on single skinfolds were also provided. The subjects used in this study averaged 22 years in age (range 17 to 25). At ages widely differing from that of the sample from which they were derived, the prediction equations will not be strictly valid.

Roentgenographic Predictors of Density

A similar approach was followed in converting roentgenographic measurements of subcutaneous fat into density and, finally, into total body fat.[27] Equations for predicting body density were calculated for the thickness of the skin-plus-subcutaneous layer measured at single sites and for the combined lateral-plus-medial or ventral-plus-dorsal thicknesses, when available. It was noted that in this sample of middle-aged men the precision with which the density could be predicted was not improved when the width of the subcutaneous fat was related to stature, to the bone width of the limb measured on the roentgenograms, or to the width of the bone-plus-muscle segment. For 4 locations the cross-sectional area of the adipose tissue was calculated and expressed as percentage the cross-sectional area of the nonadipose (lean) tissues of the limbs, again without increasing the precision with which the density (and thus total fat) could be estimated.

According to the available evidence, admittedly limited, measurements of the layer of skin with its adjoining adipose tissue made on roentgenograms of the extremities do not appear to be more effective indicators of the overall leanness-fatness than the direct (skinfold) measurements. However, a systematic appraisal in terms of prediction of total fat remains to be carried out. A comprehensive analysis of the value of roentgenographic measurements of body fat should include also sites on the trunk, not accessible to the skinfold-caliper technique. In setting up the prediction equations proper attention should be given to factors of age and sex.

Roentgenographic Appraisal of Adipose Tissue

Garn took the roentgenogrammetric bull by the horns and attempted to arrive in simpler ways at the total amount of body "fat." [37] For these purposes he considered, in Behnke's footsteps, the body mass (M) as consisting of "fat" (A) and "fat free" weight (L):

$$M = A + L$$

The symbols were supplied by the present writer in the hope of making the matters clearer. Garn's "fat" is not the fat defined as ether extract and, consequently, all comparisons with the results of densitometric and hydrometric analyses, operating with chemically defined fat, are out of order. The symbol A indicates that we deal principally with the anatomist's adipose tissue. L stands for "lean body mass," a concept more appropriate than "fat-free mass" for Garn's purposes. The basic step is the derivation of a simple equation for predicting total body weight ($\hat{M}$) from roentgenographic thicknesses (X) of the layer of skin plus subcutaneous adipose tissue:

$$\hat{M} = a + bX$$

The value "a" defines body mass, $\hat{M}$, for $X = 0$, that is the "lean body mass" (L) of the group. The constant "b" is the slope of the line of the best fit and bX_i defines the amount of roentgenographic "fat" in a given individual ($\hat{F} = bX_i$). In other words, Garn obtains an estimate of the weight of "fat," in kilograms, for an individual by multiplying the roentgenographic measurement (X_i) by the constant b.

He uses the value of calculated fat ($\hat{F}$) in conjunction with the actual body weight of an individual (M), where

$$M = \hat{F} + L$$

and defines

$$L = M - \hat{F}$$

Garn uses as predictors of weight the thickness of the iliac-crest "fat" for females and of the mid-trochanteric "fat" for males. A de-

TABLE IX

ABSOLUTE VALUES OF BODY SIZE AND BODY COMPONENTS IN
FOUR TYPES OF SUBJECTS (FROM [2])

	Trade Apprentices	A Gymnast	Emaciated Woman	Obese Woman
Height, cm.	166.9	169.3	160.2	158.0
Body weight, kg.	57.3	72.0	39.5	90.0
Skeleton, kg.	10.4	13.0	8.4	8.0
Muscles, kg.	24.5	34.6	12.7	18.8
Skin and fat, kg.	10.9	9.5	2.7	47.7
Remainder, kg.	11.5	14.9	15.6	15.4

tailed appraisal of Garn's approach and its limitations is beyond the scope of this presentation. Perhaps the really important point is the theoretical possibility of providing estimates of body composition (in terms of adipose tissue, muscle and skeleton or fat, protein, and bone mineral) on the basis of suitable roentgenograms, especially when considered in conjunction with methods allowing us to separate the total body weight into its principal components.

SOME APPLICATIONS

Because of space limitations, only illustrative findings will be cited in a limited range of topics: body build, age and sex, and nutrition.

Body Build

Human physique has several aspects—size, form, and composition. Differences in size are obvious and biologically as well as socially important, so obvious, indeed, that they have been completely left out of some of the typological systems that achieved wide popularity. Body form, a characteristic that attracted most attention, is the resultant of skeletal proportions and of the amount and distribuion of soft tissues, especially of muscles and subcutaneous adipose tissue. It has been the perennial plague of this sector of physical anthropology that typological "systems" were springing, ready-made, out of the heads of their creators. A facile synthesis tended to precede a solid analysis. Flashes of genius were more conspicuous than hard, biologically sound exploration of the basic variables and their interrelations.

When one looks at a camel and at Nilotic (Sanga) cattle one can readily observe that both have a "hump." This is as far as one can go, somatoscopically. Yet, these similarities are grossly deceptive: in one case we are looking at a fat-storing hump, in the other case at a

TABLE X

BODY COMPONENTS, AS PERCENTAGE OF GROSS BODY WEIGHT

	Trade Apprentices	A Gymnast	Emaciated Woman	Obese Woman
Skeleton	18.1	18.1	21.3	9.0
Muscles	42.8	48.0	32.2	20.9
Skin and fat	19.0	13.1	6.9	52.9
Remainder	20.1	20.8	39.6	17.2

purely muscular thickening in the cervicothoracic region. This brief excursion into the zoological realm should encourage us to pause and to evaluate more rigorously the validity of somatoscopic ratings in man.

Somatometric Estimates of Body Components

In Matiegka's (1921) system the human physique was characterized in terms of the masses of the principal compartments, anatomically defined (skeleton, muscles, skin plus subcutaneous fat) and estimated on the basis of body measurements.[2] This represents a fundamentally sound, though not exhaustive, approach to the complex problem of body build, emphasizing body composition as its crucial facet. It may be of interest to present a sample of the data obtained by Matiegka for a group of 12 apprentices, a gymnast, an emaciated and an obese woman. The absolute values of the estimated body components are given in Table IX. For purposes of comparison, the components may be expressed as percentages of body weight (Table X), or, preferably, in terms of the weight of the skeleton as the reference point (Table XI).

Relative Development of Adipose Tissue and Musculature

Matiegka's approach was "on the books" but it largely remained there. McCloy (1936) was aware of Matiegka's efforts to evaluate the amount of the various components making up the body but cited him as a measurer of skinfolds [38, p. 66]. Significant impetus to the measurement of subcutaneous fat in children was given by Fran-

TABLE XI

BODY COMPONENTS, AS PERCENTAGE OF SKELETAL WEIGHT

	Trade Apprentices	A Gymnast	Emaciated Woman	Obese Woman
Muscles	236	265	151	233
Skin and fat	105	72	33	591
Remainder	111	114	186	191

zen [38a] and a series of studies on subcutaneous tissue was undertaken at the Iowa Child Welfare Research Station in the thirties. "Total fat" was obtained as the sum of skinfold thicknesses measured at various sites. In one study the skinfold measurements were averaged and the individual deviations from the norm were multiplied by the computed surface area of the body in order to obtain a rough measure of the volume of fat over or under the norm. The matter of norms was considered in the second volume of McCloy's treatise on the appraisal of physical status.[39] The development of the musculature was assessed in two ways, in terms of the relative limb girths (without correction for subcutaneous fat) and of performance on strength tests. The norms covered childhood and adolescence (4 to 17 years) and were extended to college men and women.

Visual Appraisal of Body Types

The system of "body typing" that was most influential in the last two decades was developed by W. C. Sheldon.[40] Man's physique is characterized in terms of 3 "components" rated at a scale from 1 (minimum) to 7 (maximum): endomorphy, mesomorphy and ectomorphy. These components were derived from the study of photographs, conceptually far from the anatomist's dissection table. Sheldon strives for an assessment of an individual's "somatotype" which would closely approach the "morphogenotype" and, by definition, would represent a permanent characteristic of an individual. He would object to defining "endomorphy" simply as an anthropomorphic estimate of the amount of fat. The fact remains, and it is an important fact, that variations in endomorphy ratings are associated with individual differences in the density of the human body, a measure of the total fat content.

At the Laboratory of Physiological Hygiene, University of Minnesota, a group of young men were measured and photographed under control conditions and after losing one-fourth of their body weight. Two independent sets of ratings of the somatotype were obtained.[41] Combining all the available information (2 sets of ratings for the 2 conditions), an equation for predicting density (and thus total body fat) from ratings of endomorphy was calculated.[42] The data relating endomorphy ratings to density and body fat are given in Table 10.

Sheldon would probably criticize the authors of the ratings in that they have not taken into account adequately the "nutritional status" of the subjects. To us the fact is important that "endomorphy" ratings, made by competent investigators (including Sheldon's long-time associates, especially Dupertuis,[43]) correlate with the densitometric estimates of the fat content. This raises hopes that it will be possible to turn the tables and to develop a system of somatoscopic ratings and of measurements made on standardized photographs which will be based on and validated by methods yielding independent criteria of adipose, muscular, and skeletal masses or at least linear indicators of such masses.

Parnell's scheme, representing a combination of physical anthropology and photography, is a step in this direction.[43a] The use of somatometric data should help to provide a more precise definition of the "components" and add objectivity that is lacking when photoscopy is used alone. The body measurements include height, weight, a height-weight ratio (height/$\sqrt[3]{\text{weight}}$), biepicondylar measurements of humerus and femur as indicators of lateral bony dimensions of the extremities, two limb girths—upper arm and calf, 3 skinfolds (subscapular, suprailiac, on the back of the upper arm) and their total, and 4 trunk measurements (biacromial and bi-iliac width, chest width and chest depth).

The author aims to approach as closely as possible Sheldon's estimates of somatotypes but he has replaced the terms endomorphy, mesomorphy and ectomorphy by Fat, Muscularity and Linearity.

Lindegård's Differential Somatology

In Sweden, Lindegård[44] developed a system to which he refers as "differential somatology" (differential morphology) and which is sound in principle though the details, including the selection of the actual measurements and definition of body-build "factors," may be open to discussion. The system operates with variables chosen to reflect the individual variation in 4 aspects of physique: 1) body length (length of radius and tibia), 2) skeletal sturdiness (bicondylar breadths), 3) muscular development (from dynamometric data on grip strength, shoulder thrust and shoulder pull) and 4) adiposity, evaluated as a deviation of the actual from the predicted value of body weight or extremital girths, keeping other relevant features of body-build constant, or, more recently, from skinfolds. The basic

TABLE XII

ENDOMORPHY RATINGS OF YOUNG MEN AND THE ASSOCIATED VALUES OF
BODY DENSITY AND ESTIMATED BODY FAT

Endomorphy	1	2	3	4	5	6	7
Density	1.0871	1.0790	1.0710	1.0629	1.0549	1.0468	1.0388
Body fat, %	5	8	11	14	17	20	23

variables ("factors") are presented in the form of a "body-build diagram," with group means as reference points and standard deviations as units of measurement.

The combination of functional criteria (performance on tests of strength), used in assessment of "muscularity," in conjunction with morphological criteria on the basis of which the other body-build variables are defined, is undesirable, and, most likely, unnecessary. Measurements of the circumference of the extremities, together with skinfolds determined at the same level (perhaps with bicondylar diameters and a length factor added for a good measure) provide usable morphological indicators of muscular development, at least for the extremities.

Lindegård and his co-workers investigated the variables going into the system of classifying physiques and related the somatic individual differences to a variety of morphological, endocrinological and behavioral characteristics.[44a] They studied the distribution of subcutaneous fat and confirmed, using skinfolds measured at 10 sites, the presence of a continuum of interindividual differences in the proportion of the deposits of subcutaneous fat in the trunk and extremities (cf. B. Škerlj's Truncic-Extremital Vector).[45] Muscularity, assessed on the basis of dynamometric recordings, was examined in reference to physical activity and relations between body build and selected male sex characteristics, such as genital size and trunk hair, were studied.

Body Build and Body Functions

It is not feasible to present here in detail the data on the co-variation of body build, with its description anchored in body composition, with other somatic, biochemical, and behavioral characteristics. One or two examples must suffice.

In comparing individuals, we wish at times to eliminate the effect of absolute body size. In physiological and biochemical studies, the surface area of the body was found to be a useful point of reference. Behnke,[46] at the very outset of modern investigations on body composition, expressed the hope that "lean body mass" would be a better reference for such biologically important functions as basal oxygen consumption (basal metabolism) or blood volume. This possibility was confirmed in a study on cardiac function and body composition.[47] Thus differences in "lean body mass" accounted for about twice as much (55%) of the individual variation in cardiac output as body weight (25%), body surface being intermediate in this respect (36%).

Patterns of Soft-Tissue Distribution

In addition to the *amount* of body fat (and muscles), anthropologists have been interested in *patterns of the distribution* of soft tissues. The distribution may refer to the separation of the total into the subcutaneous and the inner fraction. There are some indications [45] that these two fractions do not remain constant throughout the life span. In the process of aging the "internal" fat, contained in the various fat depots (perirenal, pericardial, mesenteric, omental), and within the muscles, appears to increase not only absolutely, as does the subcutaneous fat, but also relatively.

From the point of view of characterizing body build, the pattern of the distribution of the subcutaneous fat over the body surface is important.[48] In order to portray this component of body form, the number of sites should be larger than when we are concerned with the overall leanness-fatness. For this purpose it is desirable to supplement skinfold measurements by soft-tissue roentgenograms of those regions, such as the trochanteric region or the thigh, which are not suitable for skinfold measurements but which show marked individual differences. It is of some interest that the pattern of thicknesses of subcutaneous fat remains fairly stable when the total size of the fat stores in the body changes.[49, 50]

Age and Sex

At least during certain phases of the life cycle, age and sex "interact": the changes in body composition with age are divergent, not parallel, for the male and female of the human species.

This was shown [51] on the basis of roentgenographic measurements of the thickness of subcutaneous adipose tissue. The "outer fat" was measured on the lower thorax. The age trends, using median rather than average values because of the marked skewness of the fat-distributions, are indicated in Figure 28.

At the age of 6 years the fat layer is somewhat thicker in girls. This difference of about 1 mm. is maintained, on the absolute basis, from the 6th to the 11th year, a period in which there is a parallel increase in fat on the lower thorax in both sexes. From the 11th to the 18th year the fat on the lower thorax continued to increase in girls, up to a value of 9 mm., while in boys the fat thickness became stabilized during this period at about 4.5 mm.

Suggestive evidence of the substantial differences in the fat content of adult men and women was provided by a co-worker of R. E.

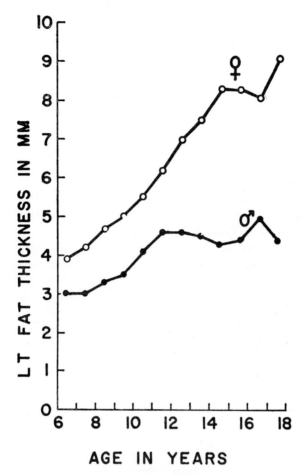

Figure 28. Continuous increase in lower thoracic (LT) fat in girls and parallel increase in boys, terminating at 11.5 years. By 14.5 years the adult female/male ratio of 180 per cent has been attained.[51]

Scammon at Minnesota.[52] The data are given in Table XIII. The weight of the skin is somewhat larger in men than in women, as would be expected. When the skin weight is used as the reference point, it becomes clearly evident that women have substantially larger deposits of subcutaneous adipose tissue than men. In view of the small number of observations these data would be of little relevance were they not confirmed by much other evidence (see, e.g., [53]).

Densitometric studies indicate that both men [54] and women [55] ex-

TABLE XIII

WEIGHT OF SKIN AND OF THE SUBCUTANEOUS TISSUE (TELA SUBCUTANEA) IN ADULT MEN AND WOMEN (FROM [52])

	Men	Women	Women/Men
Number	13	2	
Mean age, years	37	39	
Mean skin weight, kg.	3.290	3.000	0.91
Mean weight of tela subcutanea, kg.	6.604	11.897	1.80
$100 \dfrac{\text{tela subcutanea}}{\text{skin weight}}$	201	397	1.98

hibit a marked increase in the fat content with age. The striking sex difference is maintained throughout the period of maturity. The data are summarized in Table XIV.

The downward age trends in the density of both sexes are unmistakable and are due, to a very large degree, to the accumulation of body fat. The numerical interpretation of this trend in terms of the fat content is somewhat uncertain, especially as far as the calculation of fat percentages for women is concerned. Nevertheless, the existence of substantial sex differences in fatness and the presence of fat gains in the process of aging, at least in the U.S., may be regarded as well established.

Nutrition

The potential impact of diet on physique has been brought out

TABLE XIV

AGE, SEX, DENSITY AND ESTIMATED FAT CONTENT, AS PER CENT OF BODY WEIGHT ([54], [55])

	Men				
N	*21*	*25*	*29*	*44*	*34*
Age range	18–22	23–29	45–47	48–52	53–57
Mean age, years	20.3	25.2	46.0	50.0	54.6
Relative body weight, %	100.0	99.9	100.2	99.9	100.2
Density	1.072	1.063	1.047	1.044	1.041
Fat, %	11	14	20	21	22

	Women		
N	*23*	*19*	*20*
Age range	18–30	31–45	46–67
Mean age, years	24.2	39.1	56.0
Relative body weight, %	95.3	97.3	95.3
Density	1.040	1.027	1.016
Fat, %	23	28	32

TABLE XV

CALORIC EQUIVALENTS OF WEIGHT LOSSES (CAL./KG) AT DIFFERENT
INTERVALS OF CALORIC RESTRICTION

Experiment	Caloric intake, Cal./day	Period, Days				
		1–3	4–7	7–12	11–13	22–24
'53	580	2996	4260	5616		
'54	1010	2596			7043	8700

dramatically by animal studies: Different "planes of nutrition" not only produce animals of greatly different weights at the same age, but also of vastly different conformation and composition.[56] This fact is of basic importance for a reassessment of the concept of "genetically determined body build" and brings out its limitations. The matter is so important, even though we admittedly deal with extremes rarely if ever found in human nutrition, that the findings should be cited in full: "In general, cattle reared on a low plane of nutrition retain juvenile form; they are leggy, narrow and shallow in the body, especially in the hind quarters, with long, large heads, as compared with animals of the same breed, even identical twins, which are reared on a high plane of nutrition. As in sheep, limited nutritive supply largely inhibits the normal development of secondary sexual characters" [56, p. 498]. The principal tissues as well as the various internal organs are affected to a different degree by the restriction of the nutritive supply, fat depots being affected most, the central nervous system least.

When studied over a period of time, the adult human body—its weight and its composition—will reflect the supply of nutrients relative to the physiological requirements. Consequently, gross body composition may be used as a measure, partial and incomplete, to be sure, of "nutritional status." When the food intake exceeds the caloric needs, the excess calories are stored in the body in the form of body fat. When the caloric requirements exceed the supply, the body must cover the deficit from its own stores. Actually, under these conditions, the changes in body composition are quite complex, depending on the rate and duration of the positive or negative energy "balance," and on the availability of other nutrients which affect food utilization or water storage.

Composition of Rapid Weight Loss or Weight Gain

Dramatic changes in the composition of tissues lost when normal young men performed work on low calorie carbohydrate diets are portrayed in Table XV. These data were obtained in the course of 2 studies during which 6 men were maintained for 12 days on 580 calories per day and 13 men were given daily 1010 calories for a total of 24 days. The actual daily caloric expenditure was about 3200 cal./day.[57]

The caloric deficit was defined as the difference between the caloric equivalent of the food eaten and the energy expended over a specified period. The ratio of the caloric deficit to the weight lost, indicating the caloric value of the weight loss, changes progressively in the course of caloric restriction. The daily negative energy balance (caloric deficit) decreased only moderately, from about 1860 cal. on the sixth day of the '54 experiment to 1420 on the 24th day. In the first days of restriction the weight losses were relatively large, so that the calorie equivalents (Δ calories/Δ weight) were low. This clearly indicates a large proportion of materials, principally water, that were present in the weight loss but yielded relatively little or no energy. As restriction progressed, larger and larger proportions of the weight loss corresponded to materials yielding large amounts of energy per unit of weight, principally fat (Table XV). Oxidation of fat alone would be expected to yield about 9450 calories per kilogram of fat oxidized.

During refeeding the trend was reversed. A large part of the early gain was again made up of water. Toward the end of the recovery period it appears that fat and protein must have been stored in the body in spite of the fact that no net gain in body weight was observed at that time. It is probable that during this period the actual gain of fat (and protein), reflecting the clearly established positive energy (and nitrogen) balance, was masked by a concurrent loss of body water.

There is no doubt about the qualitative character of the changes

TABLE XVI

Composition of Mean Daily Weight Losses at Different Periods of the '54 Experiment [57] Estimated by Combining Data on Weight Losses with Determinations of Energy Balance and Urinary Nitrogen Excretion (Used for Computation of the Amount of Protein that was Oxidized)

	Period of Caloric Restriction, Days		
	1 to 3	11 to 13	22 to 24
Weight loss/day, kg.	0.800	0.233	0.167
Fat	25	69	85
Protein	5	12	15
Water	70	19	0

TABLE XVII

MEAN BODY WEIGHT, IN KG., AND BODY DENSITY IN THE MINNESOTA EXPERIMENT
ON PROLONGED CALORIC RESTRICTION (S) AND NUTRITIONAL REHABILITATION (R).
THE NUMBERS FOLLOWING THE PERIOD SYMBOLS (E.G., S12) INDICATE THE
APPROXIMATE WEEK DURING WHICH THE MEASUREMENTS WERE MADE.
N = 32 MEN

Period	Control	S12	S24	R12
Weight	69.34	57.77	53.63	59.76
Density	1.067	1.080	1.085	1.074

in the composition of the weight loss, computed on the basis of figures for energy expenditure and food intake. Is it possible to estimate the actual composition of the weight loss?

The results of such an analysis are presented in Table XVI. The weight loss per day decreased by the 24th day to less than one-fourth of the initial daily weight decrement. At the same time, the composition changed profoundly, especially as far as the proportions of water and fat are concerned.

These results are presented here for three reasons:

1) To indicate the complexity of what might appear as a simple problem of rapid weight loss or weight gain.
2) To point out the changing composition of the weight gained or lost at different periods of caloric restriction or refeeding.
3) To stress the occasional necessity, without going into the details of methodology, of combining anthropometric data with information obtained by the physiologist (energy expenditure) and the biochemist (amount of protein oxidized), i.e. the necessity of interdisciplinary (team) research.

Effects of Prolonged Caloric Restriction and Refeeding

Profound changes in body weight, in physical appearance, external dimensions, and in body composition were observed in 32 young men, all volunteers, in the course of 24 weeks of caloric restriction, resulting in the loss of about one-quarter of the control body weight.[58] The period of follow-up studies during refeeding extended, for different individuals, from 12 to 58 weeks.

The values of body weight, in kg., and of body density during the control period (C), after 12 and 24 weeks of caloric restriction (S), and 12 weeks of refeeding (R) are given for the group of 32 subjects in Table XVII. The trends noted during restriction (decrease in weight, rise in body density) are reversed during nutritional rehabilitation. The tabular values were not corrected either for increased hydration (expansion of the extracellular fluid), manifest in a large number of subjects as a clinically recognizable edema, or for the relative increase in the bony mass. The numerical interpretation of density in terms of body fat under these conditions is anything but a straightforward matter.[59] However, the trends in density are in agreement with the body measurements.

Photographs, taken under the direction of the present writer, were measured by G. Lasker [60] and somatotyped by inspection at the Harvard Anthropometric Laboratory in cooperation with James M. Andrews IV. Both sets of ratings confirm the decrement in "roundedness" (endomorphy) and increase in "linearity" (ectomorphy) (Table XVIII).

The body dimensions that showed substantial changes as a result of caloric restriction are presented in Table XIX for a typical subject.[61] They indicate the rapid growth of soft-tissues, principally the subcutaneous fat, during the 12th to 20th week of refeeding (R12 to R20) when all imposed restrictions on caloric intake were removed. At R16 the abdominal circumference exceeded the control value although the weight barely reached the control level. Changes in abdominal circumference paralleled the alterations in body fat estimated from density. The weight (and the abdominal circumference) continued to increase and by R33 body weight exceeded the control level by almost 10 kg.

Data for subjects measured at R58 indicated a tendency toward return to pre-experimental values of body weight and body composition, even though the fat content was still somewhat elevated. The overall trend of changes in body fat, expressed as percentages of the

TABLE XVIII

AVERAGE CHANGES IN SHELDON'S "COMPONENTS" OF HUMAN PHYSIQUE
RESULTING FROM PROLONGED CALORIC DEFICIT

Period	Ratings Based on Measurements of Photographs		
	Endomorphy	Mesomorphy	Ectomorphy
Before (C)	3.38	3.78	3.28
After (S24)	1.66	2.05	5.98
Difference	−1.72	−1.73	+2.70
	Ratings Based on Somatoscopic Appraisal		
	Endomorphy	Mesomorphy	Ectomorphy
Before (C)	3.47	3.94	3.42
After (S24)	1.82	2.81	5.71
Difference	−1.65	−1.13	+2.29

TABLE XIX

Weight and Body Dimensions, in cm., of a Typical Subject [61]. C = control
S = weeks of Caloric Deficiency, R = Weeks of Refeeding

	C	S12	S24	R12	R16	R20	R33
Weight	64.7	55.8	52.1	54.2	64.5	68.9	74.1
Bideltoid diameter	43.2	40.0	39.0	40.0	43.4	44.8	
Circumferences:							
Chest	87.1	80.6	79.1				
Abdomen	75.4	70.5	70.8*	73.5	81.0	82.3	
Upper Arm	28.6	24.0	21.5	22.8	27.3	28.6	
Thigh	45.7	40.6	38.8	39.2	45.4	47.4	
Calf	37.5	35.1	34.0	34.5	37.8	38.2	

*"Bloated"

control value, is summarized in Table XX. The fat percentages represent only approximate values.

Who is Fat?

The fat content of the human body varies widely, although the full range is not well known. There are the habitually very thin individuals who sink readily ("swim like the bricklayer's chip," to use a Czech saying), with body densities exceeding 1.09, and skinfolds not much thicker than the double-thickness of the skin itself. On the other extreme there are the grossly obese individuals, with stores of adipose tissue approaching or exceeding the "lean" body weight, and effortlessly floating in water.

As to the procedures, all the approaches reviewed in the section on Methods are relevant, and others might be readily added (such as measurements of the depth of skin plus subcutaneous tissue in cadavers on cuts made to the underlying bony or muscular tissues). What is needed is 1) provision of adequate norms and 2) appraisal of the significance of the deviations—positive and negative, large and small, at different ages—from the norm.

TABLE XX

Approximative Relative Values of Densitometrically Estimated Body Fat, as Percentage of the Control Value. S = Weeks of Caloric Restriction, R = Weeks of Refeeding. The Values are Based on the Maximum Number of Subjects Available During a Given Period

Period	C	S12	S24	R12	R16	R20	R33	R58
N	32	32	32	32	12	12	6	8
Fat, as % of control	100	46	31	65	126	152	139	110

The mortality experience of the insurance companies, based on body weight and height (see, e.g., 62) will be supplemented, in time, by data on morbidity obtained in cross-sectional investigations and in a handful of important longitudinal studies that are underway. The clarification of the relations between various criteria of health and the deviations from weight norms (obtained with due regard to skeletal body build), body composition (assessed on the basis of somatic and roentgenographic measures) and other aspects of body build is one of the major challenges to physical anthropologists of the years 1960 plus.

REFERENCES

1. HOWELLS, W. W.: Introduction (to a symposium on "nutritional anthropometry"). *Human Biol.*, 28:109, 1956.

2. MATIEGKA, J.: The testing of physical efficiency. *Am. J. Phys. Anthropol.*, 4: 223-230, 1921.

3. SCAMMON, R. E.: The measurement of the body in childhood, Ch. IV in *The Measurement of Man.* Minneapolis, U. of Minn. Press, 1930, p. 173-215.

4. BOYD, E.: *Table 2 in Outline of Physical Growth and Development.* Minneapolis, Burgess Pub. Co., 1941.

5. MOULTON, R. E.: Age and chemical development in mammals. *J. Biol. Chem.*, 57:79-97, 1923.

5a. KRAYBILL, H. F., HANKINS, O. G., and FARNSWORTH, V. M.: Adaptation of anthropometric and roentgenologic measurements for appraisement of the percentage of bone in cattle. *J. Appl. Physiol.*, 7:13-18, 1954.

6. PÁLSSON, H.: Conformation and body composition, in *Progress in the Physiology of Farm Animals.* London, Butterworths, Vol. 2, 1955, p. 430-542.

7. BEHNKE, A. R.: Physiologic studies pertaining to deep sea diving and aviation, especially in relation to the fat content and composition of the human body. *Harvey Lectures*, 37:198-226, 1941-42.

8. BEHNKE, A. R., FEEN, B. G., and WELHAM, W. C.: Specific gravity of healthy men: Body weight ÷ body volume as an index of obesity. *J. Amer. Med. Assoc.*, 118:495-498, 1942.

9. RATHBUN, E. N. and PACE, N.: Studies in body composition: I. Determination of body fat by means of the body specific gravity. *J. Biol. Chem.*, 158: 667-676, 1945.

10. PACE, N. and RATHBUN, E. N.: Studies on body composition: III. The body water and chemically combined nitrogen content in relation to fat content. *J. Biol. Chem.*, 158:685-691, 1945.

11. PACE, N., KLINE, L., SCHACHMAN, H. K., and HARFENIST, M.: Studies on body composition: IV. Use of radioactive hydrogen for measurement in vivo of total body water. *J. Biol. Chem.*, 168:459-469, 1947.

12. MACY, ICIE G.: *Nutrition and Chemical Growth in Childhood.* Springfield, Ill., Thomas, 1942, 1946, 1951.

13. MACY, ICIE G. and KELLY, HARRIET J.: *Chemical Anthropology: A New Approach to Growth in Children.* Chicago, University of Chicago Press, 1957.

13a. BROŽEK, J.: Book review of *Chemical Anthropology.* Am. J. Phys. Anthropol., n.s. 16:489-493, 1958.

14. KEYS, A. and BROŽEK, J.: Body fat in adult man. *Physiol. Rev.,* 33:245-325, 1953.

15. STUART, H. C., HILL, P. and SHAW, C.: Growth of bone, muscle and overlying tissues as revealed by studies of roentgenograms of the leg area. Monogr. Soc. Research Child Develop. No. 26, 1940.

16. REYNOLDS, E. L.: Distribution of subcutaneous fat in childhood and adolescence. Monogr. Soc. Research Child Develop. No. 50, 1951.

17. TANNER, J. M.: *Growth at Adolescence.* Springfield, Ill., Thomas, 1955.

18. GARN, S. M. and SHAMIR, Z.: *Methods for Research on Human Growth.* Springfield, Ill., Thomas, 1958.

19. MITCHELL, H. H., HAMILTON, T. S., STEGGERDA, F. R., and BEAN, H. W.: Chemical composition of the adult human body and its bearing on the biochemistry of growth. *J. Biol. Chem.,* 158:625-637, 1945.

20. FORBES, R. M., COOPER, A. R., and MITCHELL, H. H.: The composition of the adult human body as determined by chemical analysis. *J. Biol. Chem.,* 203:359-366, 1953.

21. WIDDOWSON, E. M., McCANCE, R. A., and SPRAY, C. M.: Chemical composition of the human body. *Clin. Sci.,* 10:113-125, 1951.

22. STEWART, T. D., ed.: *Hrdlička's Practical Anthropometry,* 4th edition. Philadelphia, Wistar Institute, 1952.

23. TANNER, J. M. and WHITEHOUSE, R. H.: The Harpenden skinfold caliper. *Am. J. Phys. Anthropol.,* n.s. 13:743-746, 1955.

23a. Association of Life Insurance Medical Directors and Actuarial Society of America: *Medico-Actuarial Investigations,* Vol. 1, 1912.

24. Committee on Nutritional Anthropometry Food and Nutrition Board, National Research Council: Recommendations concerning body measurements for the characterization of nutritional status. *Human Biol.,* 28:115-123, 1956.

25. BROŽEK, J.: Physique and nutritional status of adult men. *Human Biol.,* 28:124-140, 1956.

26. TROTTER, M.: A preliminary study of estimation of the weight of the skeleton. *Am. J. Phys. Anthropol.,* n.s. 12:537-552, 1954.

26a. MERZ, A. L., TROTTER, M., and PETERSON, R. R.: Estimation of skeletal weight in the living. *Am. J. Phys. Anthropol.,* n.s. 14:589-609, 1956.

26b. FALKNER, F. and WISDOM, S.: Measurement of tissue components radiologically. *Brit. Med. J.,* 2:1240, 1952.

27. BROŽEK, J. and MORI H.: Some interrelations between somatic, roentgenographic and densitometric criteria of fatness. *Human Biol.,* 30:322-336, 1958.

28. GARN, S. M.: Fat patterning and fat intercorrelations in the adult male. *Human Biol.,* 26:59-69, 1954.

29. BROŽEK, J., HENSCHEL, A., and KEYS, A.: Effect of submersion in water on the volume of residual air in man. *J. Appl. Physiol.,* 2:240-246, 1949.

30. SIRI, W. E.: Apparatus for measuring human body volume. *Rev. Sci. Instruments*, 27:729-738, 1956.
31. BROŽEK, J.: Changes in body composition in man during maturity and their nutritional implications. *Federation Proc.*, 11:784-793, 1952.
32. KEYS, A., ANDERSON, J. T., and BROŽEK, J.: Weight gain from simple overeating. I. Character of the tissue gained. *Metabolism*, 4:427-432, 1955.
32a. FIDANZA, F., KEYS, A., and ANDERSON, J. T.: Density of body fat in man and other mammals. *J. Appl. Physiol.*, 6:252-256, 1953.
33. BROŽEK, J.: Measurement of body compartments in nutritional research: Comment on selected methods, in *Methods for Evaluation of Nutritional Adequacy and Status*. Washington, Nat. Acad. Sci.-Nat. Res. Council, 1954, p. 265-279.
34. BEHNKE, A. R.: Body composition, in *Methods for Evaluation of Nutritional Adequacy and Status*. Washington, Nat. Acad. Sci.-Nat. Res. Council, 1954, p. 294-310.
35. BROŽEK, J. and KEYS, A.: The evaluation of leanness-fatness in man: Norms and interrelationships. *Brit. J. Nutr.*, 5:194-206, 1951.
36. PASCALE, L. R., GROSSMAN, M. L., SLOANE, H. S., and FRANKEL, T.: Correlations between thickness of skinfolds and body density in 88 soldiers. *Human Biol.*, 28:165-176, 1956.
37. GARN, S. M.: Roentgenogrammetric determinations of body composition. *Human Biol.*, 29:337-353, 1957.
38. McCLOY, C. H.: *Appraising Physical Status: The Selection of Measurements*. Iowa City, Iowa, University of Iowa, 1936.
38a. FRANZEN, R.: *Physical Measures of Growth and Nutrition*. New York, American Child Health Association, 1927.
39. McCLOY, C. H.: *Appraising Physical Status: Methods and Norms*. Iowa City, Iowa, University of Iowa, 1938.
40. SHELDON, W. C.: *Varieties of Human Physique*. New York, Harper, 1940.
41. LASKER, G. W.: Effects of partial starvation on somatotypes. *Am. J. Phys. Anthropology*, n.s. 5:323-341, 1947.
42. BROŽEK, J.: Role of anthropometry in the study of body composition: Toward a synthesis of methods. *Ann. N.Y. Acad. Sci.*, 63, Art. 4:491-504, 1955.
43. DUPERTUIS, C. W., PITTS, G. C., OSSERMAN, E. F., WELHAM, W. C., and BEHNKE, A. R.: Relation of specific gravity to body build in a group of healthy men. *J. Appl. Physiol.*, 3:676-680, 1951.
43a. PARNELL, R. W.: *Behaviour and Physique: An Introduction to Practical and Applied Somatometry*. London, E. Arnold, 1958.
44. LINDEGÅRD, B.: *Variations in Human Body-Build*. Copenhagen, Munksgaard, Acta Psychiatr. Neurol., Suppl. 96, 1953.
44a. LINDEGÅRD, B., ed.: *Body-Build, Body-Function, and Personality*. Lund, Lunds Universitets et Årsskrift, 1955.
45. ŠKERLJ, B., BROŽEK, J., and HUNT, E. E., JR.: Subcutaneous fat and age changes in body build and body form in women. *Am. J. Phys. Anthropol.*, n.s. 11:577-600, 1953.
46. BEHNKE, A. R.: Physiologic studies pertaining to deep sea diving and aviation, especially in relation to the fat content and composition of the human body. *Harvey Lect.*, 37:198-226, 1941-42.

47. Taylor, H. L., Brožek, J., and Keys, A.: Basal cardiac function and body composition, with special reference to obesity. *J. Clin. Investigation, 31:* 976-983, 1952.

48. Garn, S. M.: Relative fat patterning: An individual characteristic. *Human Biol., 27:*75-89, 1955.

49. Garn, S. M.: Applications of pattern analysis to anthropometric data. *Annals N.Y. Acad. Sci., 63:*537-552, 1955.

50. Garn, S. M. and Brožek, J.: Fat changes during weight loss. *Science, 124:* 682, 1956.

51. Garn, S. M. and Haskell, Joan, A.: Fat changes during adolescence. *Science, 126:*1615-1616, 1959.

52. Wilmer, H. A.: Quantitative growth of skin and subcutaneous tissue in relation to human surface area. *Proc. Soc. Exper. Biol. Med., 43:*386-388, 1940.

53. Reynolds, E. L. and Grote, P.: Sex differences in the distribution of tissue components in the human leg from birth to maturity. *Anat. Record, 102:* 45-53, 1948.

54. Brožek, J.: Changes of body composition in man during maturity and their nutritional implications. *Federation Proc., 11:*788-793, 1952.

55. Brožek, J., Chen, K. P., Carlson, W., and Bronczyk, F.: Age and sex differences in man's fat content during maturity. *Federation Proc., 12:* 21-22, 1953.

56. Pálsson, H.: Conformation and body composition, in *Progress in the Physiology of Farm Animals,* Vol. 2. London, Butterworths, 1955, p. 430-542.

57. Brožek, J., Grande, F., Taylor, H. L., Anderson, J. T., Buskirk, E. R., and Keys, A.: Changes in body weight and body dimensions in men performing work on a low calorie carbohydrate diet. *J. Appl. Physiol., 10:*412-420, 1957.

58. Keys, A., Brožek, J., Henschel, A., Mickelsen, O., and Taylor, H. L.: *The Biology of Human Starvation.* Minneapolis, University of Minnesota Press, 1950.

59. Brožek, J.: Changes in specific gravity and body fat of young men under conditions of experimental semi-starvation. *Federation Proc., 5:*13, 1946.

60. Lasker, G.: Effects of partial starvation on somatotype. *Am. J. Phys. Anthropol., n.s. 5:*323-341, 1947.

61. Brožek, J.: Starvation and nutritional rehabilitation: A quantitative case study. *J. Amer. Diet. Assoc., 28:*917-926, 1952.

62. Marks, H. H.: Body weight: Facts from life insurance records. *Human Biol., 28:*217-231, 1956.

FOR FURTHER READING, CONSULT:

Brožek, J.: Measuring nutriture. *Am. J. Phys. Anthropol., n.s. 11:*147-180, 1953.
Clarifies the role of anthropometry in the assessment of "nutritional status" and the far-reaching implications of "nutritional anthropometry" for physical anthropology. The consideration of nutrition (and activity) injects into physical anthropology concern for *interpretation* of body dimensions, their etiology and biomedical significance.

BROŽEK, J., ed.: *Body Measurements and Human Nutrition.* Detroit, Wayne State University Press, 1956.

Contains recommendations concerning anthropometric assessment of nutritional status, plus 11 papers on obesity and body composition. Constitutes the final report of the Committee on Nutritional Anthropometry (Food and Nutrition Board, National Research Council).

BROŽEK, J. and HENSCHEL, A., eds.: *Body Composition: Appraisal of Methods* (in press). Detroit, Wayne State University Press, 1960.

Proceedings of symposium, held under the sponsorship of the Advisory Board on Quartermaster Research and Development, National Academy of Sciences—National Research Council in January, 1959. An up-to-date, comprehensive assessment of the complex methodology.

CURETON, T. K.: *Physical Fitness of Champion Athletes.* Urbana, University of Illinois Press, 1951, esp. p. 13-27.

The Cureton Modified Somatotype System reduces Sheldon's scheme to a two-dimensional system of thinness-fatness (linearity vs. ponderosity) as one variable (based on measurements of skinfolds, girths, weight/height ratio or vital capacity) and strength, as the other variable. Considerations of body build in reference to physical exercise represent an important area of applied physical anthropology.

EPPRIGHT, E. S., SWANSON, P., and IVERSON, C. A., eds.: *Weight Control.* Ames, Iowa State College Press, 1955.

A collection of papers on different aspects of weight control, including appraisal of obesity and its significance as a health hazard.

SPECTOR, H., PETERSON, M. S., and FRIEDEMANN, T. E., eds.: *Methods for Evaluation of Nutritional Adequacy and Status.* Washington, National Academy of Sciences—National Research Council, 1954.

In the section dealing with body composition (pp. 265-313) the quantitative assumptions in the densitometric and hydrometric system of body composition analysis are spelled out in detail.

FORSSMAN, O. and LINDEGÅRD, B.: The post-coronary patient: A multi-disciplinary investigation of middle-aged Swedish males. *J. Psychosomat. Res.,* 3:89-169, 1958.

Application of Lindegård's system of quantitative description of body build in terms of 4 "factors" (length, sturdiness, muscularity, fatness), in a biomedical context.

DIRECTORIES

International Directory of Anthropological Institutions

Published in 1953 by the Wenner-Gren Foundation for Anthropological Research, New York, and obtainable from the American Anthropological Association, William Godfrey, Jr., Executive Secretary, Logan Museum, Beloit College, Beloit, Wisconsin. Price $12.50.

International Directory of Anthropologists

Obtainable from the Secretary, Division of Anthropology and Psychology, National Research Council, 2101 Constitution Avenue, Washington 21, D.C. Price $3.00.

Yearbook of Anthropology 1955

Published by the Wenner-Gren Foundation for Anthropological Research, 14 East 71st Street, New York 21, New York. Containing a world coverage of anthropology, with data on dissertations, awards, and professional organizations.

SOME CURRENT ANTHROPOLOGICAL PERIODICALS EITHER WHOLLY OR IN PART DEVOTED TO PHYSICAL ANTHROPOLOGY

Acta Geneticae Medicae et Gemellogiae

Published quarterly, an international journal devoted to the publication of research in human genetics and multiple births. Instituto Gregorio Mendel di Roma, Largo Dell'Amba, Aradam 1, Roma. Annual subscription Lire 7,000 ($18.00).

Actas y Memorias de la Sociedad Española de Antropologia, Etnografia y Prehistoria

Published irregularly by the Sociedad Española de Antropología, Etnografia y Prehistoria, Paseo de Atocha 11, Madrid, Spain.

Acta Genetica et Statistica Medica

Published quarterly by S. Karger Ltd. Holbeinstrasse 22, Basel, Switzerland. Annual subscription 44 Swiss francs.

American Anthropologist

Published six times a year by the American Anthropological Association. Executive Secretary, William S. Godfrey, Jr., Logan Museum, Beloit College, Beloit, Wisconsin. Annual subscription by membership in the Association $8.50.

American Antiquity

Published quarterly by the Society for American Archeology. David A. Barreis, Sterling Hall, University of Wisconsin, Madison 6, Wisconsin. Annual subscription, $8.00.

American Journal of Human Genetics

Published quarterly by the American Society of Human Genetics, Mount Royal and Guilford Avenues, Baltimore 2, Maryland. Annual subscription $10.00.

American Journal of Physical Anthropology

Published quarterly by the Wistar Institute of Anatomy and Biology, Philadelphia, Pennsylvania. Organ of the American Association of Physical Anthropologists. Annual subscription $7.50.

Annals of Human Genetics

Formerly *Annals of Eugenics*. A journal of human genetics of considerable anthropological interest. Published quarterly by the Galton Laboratory, University College, Gower Street, London, W.C. 1., England. Subscription per volume £5 ($17.50).

Anthropological Quarterly

A journal of general anthropology edited by the Department of Anthropology, and published by the Catholic University of America, Washington, D.C. Annual subscription $3.00.

Anthropologie Différentielle et Sciences de Types Constitutionnels.

Published by the Bureau International d'Anthropologie Différentielle, Geneva, Switzerland.

L'Anthropologie

Published bi-monthly by the Société d'Anthropologie de Paris through Masson et cie., 120, Boulevard Saint-Germain, Paris Vle, France. Francs 6,000 ($17.00).

Anthropologischer Anzeiger

Published quarterly by the E. Schweitzerbart'sche Verlagsbuchhandlung, Johannerstrass 3/1, Stuttgart W, Germany. A review of the biological-anthropological literature. Subscription per volume 54DM ($12.00).

The Anthropologist

Published quarterly by the Department of Anthropology, Delhi University, Delhi, India.

Antropologia y Etnographia

Published quarterly by the Instituto Bernardino de Sahagùn de Antropologia y Etnografia, Madrid, Spain.

Anthropos

International review of ethnology and linguistics. Published irregularly with the support of the University of Freibourg, Poisieux-Froideville, Ct. de Freibourg, Switzerland. Each issue separately priced.

Antiquity

A quarterly review of archeology, published by H. W. Edwards, Ashmore Green, Newbury, Berks, England. Annual subscription 30s ($5.00).

Archiv der Julius Klaus-Stiftung für Vererbungsforschung, Sozialanthropologie und Rassenhygiene

Published quarterly by the Kuratorium der Julius Kalus Stiftung, Gemindestrasse 5, Zürich 7, Switzerland.

Archives Suisses d'Anthropologie Générale

Published bi-annually by the Institut d'Anthropologie de l'Université de Genève, 44c rue de Maraîchers, Geneva, Switzerland. 20 Swiss francs an issue.

Arquivo de Anatomia e Antropologia

Published irregularly by the Instituto de Anatomia de Lisbon, Lisbon, Portugal.

Archivo per l'Antropologia e la Etnologia

Published by the Società Italiana di Antropologia e Etnolgia, Via del Proconsolo 12, Firenze, Italy.

Archivo Iberoamericano de Historia de la Medicina y Antropologia Medica

Published quarterly by the Instituto "Arnaldo de Vilanova" de Historia de la Medicina, Duque de Midinaceli, 4, Madrid, Spain. Annual subscription 140 pesettas ($4.00).

Biological Abstracts. Section H—Human Biology

Published monthly during the months January to May, October and November; bi-monthly June to September; semi-monthly in December, by Biological Abstracts, Executive Office, University of Pennsylvania, Philadelphia 4, Pennsylvania. Annual subscription $7.50.

Biometrika

Published bi-annually by the Biometrika Office, Galton Laboratory, University College, Gower Street, London, W.C.1, England. Annual subscription 54s. ($8.00).

Biotypologie

Published quarterly by the Société de Biotypologie, Laboratoire de Biometrie, 41, rue Gay Lussac, Paris, 5e. Annual subscription 1000 francs ($3.50).

Boletin Bibliografico de Antropologia Americana

Published annually by the Instituto Panamericano de Geografia e Historia, Avenida del Oservatorio Num. 192, Tacubaya, D. F. Republica Mexicana.

British Journal of Preventive and Social Medicine

Published quarterly by the British Medical Association, Tavistock Square, London, W.C. 1. Annual subscription 25s. ($4.00).

Bulletin de la Société Préhistorique Française

Published bi-monthly by the Société Préhistorique Française, Siège Social, 250, rue Saint-Jacques, Paris-Ve, France. Annual subscription 200 francs.

Bulletins et Mémoires de la Société d'Anthropologie de Paris

Published quarterly by the *Société d'Anthropologie de Paris* through Masson et Cie., 120, Boulevard Saint-Germain, 120, Paris-VIe, France. ($2.50).

Child Development Abstracts and Bibliography

Issued three times a year by the Society for Research in Child Development, Inc., at Child Development Publications, Purdue University, Lafayette, Indiana. Annual subscription $6.00.

Current Anthropology

Published six times a year. A world journal of the sciences of man. Office, Department of Anthropology, University of Chicago, 1159 East 26th Street, Chicago 37, Illinois. Annual subscription $10.00. Special rates to students and anthropologists.

The Eastern Anthropologist

A journal founded in 1948 devoted to the study of the physical and cultural anthropology of the peoples of India. Published quarterly by the Ethnographic and Folk Culture Society, Lucknow, India. Distributed by the Biotechnic Press, Ltd., BCM/Biotechnic, London, W.C. 1, England. Annual subscription 20s ($2.80).

The Eugenics Quarterly

Published quarterly by the American Eugenics Society, 230 Park Avenue, New York 17, New York. Annual subscription $5.00.

The Eugenics Review

Organ of the Eugenics Society. Published quarterly by The Eugenics Society, 69 Eccleston Square, London, W. 1, England. Annual subscription 20s ($3.00).

Evolution

Published quarterly by The Society for the Study of Evolution. Business office at Prince and Lemon Street, Lancaster, Pennsylvania. Annual subscription $6.00.

Excerpta Medica

Fifteen sections abstracting the whole field of medicine are published. Section 1 deals with anatomy, and anthropology, embryology, and histology. Published monthly. Excerpta Medica Foundation, 2 East 103rd Street, New York 29, New York. Annual subscription $22.50.

The Florida Anthropologist

Published quarterly by the Florida Anthropological Society, Ripley P. Bullen, Treasurer, 103 Seagle Building, Gainesville, Florida. Annual subscription. $3.00.

Homo

Devoted to the comparative study of man and human biology. Organ of the Deutschen Gesellschaft für Anthropologie. Published quarterly by the Ferdinand Enke Verlag, Stuttgart, Germany. Annual subscription RM 30.

Human Biology

Published quarterly by the Wayne State University Press, Detroit 2, Michigan. Annual subscription, $5.00.

Human Organization (formerly *Applied Anthropology*)

Published quarterly by the Society for Applied Anthropology. New York State

School of Industrial and Labor Relations, Cornell University, New York. Annual subscription $6.00.

Journal de Génétique Humaine

A quarterly founded in 1953, published by the Editions Medicine et Hygiene, Geneva, Switzerland. Annual subscription 3,000 French francs ($10.00).

Journal of Forensic Medicine

Published quarterly by Juta & Co., Ltd. P.O. Box 30, Cape Town, South Africa. Annual subscription 42s ($6.00).

The Journal of Heredity

Published monthly by the American Genetic Association, 32nd Street and Elm Avenue, Baltimore 11, Maryland and 1507 M St., Washington, D.C. Annual subscription $7.00.

Journal of the Royal Anthropological Institute

Published quarterly by the Royal Anthropological Institute, 21, Bedford Square, London, W.C. 1, England. Annual subscription 63s. ($9.50).

Man

A record of anthropological science, published monthly by the Royal Anthropological Institute, 21, Bedford Square, London, W.C. 1, England. Annual subscription 30s. ($5.00).

Mankind

Official journal of the anthropological societies of Australia. Published irregularly by the Anthropological Society of New South Wales, Sydney Municipal Library, George Street, Sydney, New South Wales, Australia. Annual subscription 7s 6d. ($1.75).

Man in India

A quarterly founded in 1921, 18, Church Road, Ranchi, E. Ry. Bihar, India. Annual subscription 25s ($4.00).

Mitteilungen der Anthropologischen Gesellschaft in Wien

One to three numbers per volume per annum. Published by Anthropologischer Gesellschaft in Wien, Wien 1, Burgring 7, Austria. Annual subscription 75 schillung.

Monographs of the Society for Research in Child Development

Published irregularly by the Society for Research in Child Development. Child Development Publications, Purdue University, Lafayette, Indiana. Annual subscription $6.00.

Oceania

A journal devoted to the study of the native peoples of Australia, New Guinea and the islands of the Pacific Ocean. Published quarterly by the University of Sydney, New South Wales, Australia. Annual subscription 40s. ($6.00).

Praehistorische Zeitschrift

Published at intervals annually by Walter de Gryter & Co., Berlin W 35, Germany.

Quaternaria

Published quarterly. Via Caccini, Rome, Italy. Annual subscription 5000 lire ($8.25).

Revista Colombiana de Antropología

Published by the Instituto Colombiana de Antropología, Bogotá.

Revista de Antropologia

Published quarterly by the Universidad de São Paulo, Brazil.

Rivista di Antropologia

Published irregularly by the Instituto Italiano di Antropologia, Città Universitaria, Roma, Italia.

Revista Colombiana de Antropologia

Published annually by Instituto Colombiana de Antropologia, Apartado Nal. 407. Bogotá, Colombia. Distributed without charge.

Revue Anthropologique

Published irregularly by the Institut International D'Anthropologie. Libraire Jouve, 15 Rue Racine Paris 6°, France.

La Revue de Géographie Humaine et d'Ethnologie

A quarterly containing much valuable material of interest to the physical anthropologist. Office of publication: 5, rue Sébastien-Bottin, Paris VII, France. Annual subscription 1,740 francs ($5.50).

Runa, Archivo para Las Cienias d Hombre

A quarterly covering the whole field of anthropology. Office of publication: calle Reconquista 572 Buenos Aires, Brazil. Annual subscription $6.00.

Southwestern Journal of Anthropology

Published quarterly by the University of New Mexico Press, Albuquerque, New Mexico. Annual subscription $4.00.

S.A.S. (Bulletin du Comité International pour la Standardisation Anthropologique Synthetique)

Sovetskaia Antropologiia

A quarterly first published in 1958 by the Institute of Anthropology of Moscow State University. Obtainable through Collet's Russian Bookshop, 45 Museum Street, London, W.C.1, England. Annual subscription $6.02.

Statistical Bulletin

Published monthly by the Metropolitan Life Insurance Company, 1, Madison Avenue, New York 10, New York. Obtainable upon request.

Trabajos del Instituto Bernardino de Sahgún, de Antropologia y Etnologia

Published by the Consejo Superior de Investigaciones Cientificas, Instituto Bernardino de Sahagun, Paseo de Atocha, 11, Madrid, Spain.

Trabalhos de Antropologia e Etnologia

Published irregularly by the Instituto de Antropologia. Faculdade de Ciéncias. Oporto, Portugal.

Zeitschrift für Menschliche-Vererbungs-und Konstitutionslehre

Published quarterly by Springer-Verlag, Heidelberg, Germany. Annual subscription DM 88.40.

Zeitschrift für Morphologie und Anthropologie

Published quarterly by E. Schweitzerbart'sche Verlagsbuchhandlung, Stuttgart, Germany. Each number differently priced. Annual cost varies from $30 to $40.

List of Anthropological Periodicals, Serial, and Monograph Publications

An exhaustive, though not entirely complete, list of the many university, public, private, and museum publications of this sort will be found in *The Journal of the Royal Anthropological Institute*, Vol. 76, 1946, pp. 189-210. This list is published as from June 1949.

WORKS ON ANTHROPOMETRY AND ANTHROPOSCOPY

BRUES, A. M.: Identification of skeletal remains. *J. Crim. Law, Criminol. & Police Sci.*, 48:551-563, 1958.
A good general discussion.

GARN, S. M.: The measurement of skin temperature. *Am. J. Phys. Anthropol.*, n.s., 12:1-4, 1954.
A review and practically oriented discussion of the necessity and reason for taking skin temperature in anthropometric studies.

———— and SHAMIR, Z.: *Methods for Research in Human Growth.* Springfield, Thomas, 1958.
A useful work oriented to studies and growth.

GAVAN, J. A., WASHBURN, S. L. and LEWIS, P. H.: Photography: an anthropometric tool. *Am. J. Phys. Anthropol.*, n.s., 10:331-353, 1952.
A method of taking standardized photographs of the human body, from which accurate anthropometric measurements may be secured.

GODYCKI, M.: Sur la certitude de détermination du sexe d'après le fémur, le cubitus, et l'humérus. *Bull. et Mém. de la Soc. d' Anthrop. Paris*, 8:405-410, 1957.
A valuable analysis of methods of determining sex from the long bones.

GEOGHEGAN, B.: The determination of body measurements, surface area and body volume by photography. *Am. J. Phys. Anthropol.*, n.s., 11:97-119, 1953.
A system of photogrammetric anthropometry by means of which a wide range of measurements may be obtained from photographs of subjects in certain postures, including specific gravity when body weight is known.

HERTZBERG, H. T. E., DUPERTUIS, C. W., and EMANUEL, I.: Stereophotogrammetry as an anthropometric tool. *Photogrammetric Engineering,* 23:942-947, 1957.
A method of measuring body contours in three dimensions from photograph to drawing.

HERTZBERG, H. T. E. (editor): Annotated bibliography of applied physical anthropology in human engineering. Aero Medical Laboratory, Wright-Patterson Air Force Base, Ohio, 1958, 301 pp.
A most valuable compendium of the results of applied anthropometry and biomechanics.

HOOTON, E. A.: Elementary Anthropometry, in *Up From the Ape,* 2nd edition, New York, Macmillan, 1946, p. 715-769.
An excellent introduction to general anthropometry on the skeleton and the living subject.

HRDLIČKA, A.: *Practical Anthropometry,* 4th edition (edited by T. D. Stewart). Philadelphia, Wistar Inst., 1957.
Especially useful as a reference book to the decisions of various congresses.

KROGMAN, W. M.: A Handbook of the Measurement and Interpretation of Height and Weight in the Growing Child. *Monographs of the Society for Research in Child Development,* 8:1-68, 1950.
A simply written work telling how to measure, what errors to avoid, and how to put height and weight together in the form of an index, on a growth chart, or on the Wetzel Grid.

MARTIN, R.: *Lehrbuch Der Anthropologie,* 2nd edition, 3 vols., Jena, Fischer, 1928.
The standard work on anthropometry and anthropometric methods, though somewhat out of date, and therefore to be used with caution. The third volume is entirely devoted to the literature of physical anthropology, and is an indispensable reference work. A third edition edited by Karl Saller is in process of publication.

MERRITT, E. L.: *Analytical Photogrammetry.* New York, Pitman, 1958.
A general introduction to measurement by photography.

OLIVIER, G. and PINEAU, H.: Détermination du sexe par le poids des os. *Bull. et Mém. de la Soc. d'Anthrop. Paris,* 9:329-339, 1958.
On determining sex from the weight of the individual bones of the skeleton. There are significant differences, the bones of the forearm yield perhaps the most significant of the sex differences in weight.

SUNDERMAN, F. W. and BOERNER, F.: *Normal Values in Clinical Medicine.* Philadelphia, Saunders, 1949.
A practical compendium of normal values and standards relating to the physiological functions of the human organism, with especial reference to the needs of the doctor, but of great value to the anthropologist.

SULLIVAN, L. R.: *Essentials of Anthropometry. A Handbook for Explorers and Museum Collectors.* (Revised by H. L. Shapiro.) New York, American Museum of Natural History, 1928.
A useful pocketbook devoted to the anthropometry and anthroposcopy of the living; somewhat out of date.

WILDER, H. H.: *A Laboratory Manual of Anthropometry.* Philadelphia, Blakiston, 1920.

A very useful book on the anthropometry of the skeletal and living subject, but somewhat out of date.

WORKS ON STATISTICS

ARKIN, H. and COLTON, R. R.: *Statistical Methods,* 4th edition. New York, Barnes & Noble; 1956.
A most useful distillation of the essence of statistical methods.

CHAMBERS, E. G.: *Statistical Calculation for Beginners.* New York, Cambridge University Press, 1948.
An excellent introduction, on a very elementary level.

DAHLBERG, G.: *Statistical Methods for Medical and Biological Students.* New York, Norton, 1948.
An excellent book, assuming an elementary knowledge of mathematics.

FISHER, R. A.: *Statistics for Research Workers,* 10th edition. Edinburgh, Oliver & Boyd, 1948.
The most widely used practical treatise.

FRANZBLAU, A. N.: *A Primer of Statistics for Non-Statisticians.* New York, Harcourt, Brace, 1958.
A genuinely helpful practical introduction for the non-mathematical reader.

HILL, A. B.: *Principles of Medical Statistics,* 6th edition. New York, Oxford University Press, 1955.
A first-rate elementary introduction.

KURTZ, A. K. and EDGERTON, H. A.: *Statistical Dictionary of Terms and Symbols.* New York, Wiley, 1939.
An authoritative dictionary of clear and accurate definitions of statistical terms and symbols.

LI, C. C.: *Population Genetics.* Chicago, University of Chicago Press, 1955.
A fundamental book.

————: *Introduction to Statistical Inference.* Ann Arbor, Michigan, 1957.
A non-mathematical exposition.

MAINLAND, D.: *Elementary Medical Statistics.* Philadelphia, Saunders, 1952.

MORONEY, M. G.: *Facts from Figures.* Baltimore, Penguin Books, 1951.
A helpful introduction.

PEARL, R.: *Introduction to Medical Biometry and Statistics,* 3rd edition. Philadelphia, Saunders, 1940.
A standard and invaluable work, especially useful to physical anthropologists and medical men.

RAO, C. R.: *Advanced Statistical Methods in Biometrical Research.* New York, Wiley, 1957.
A valuable work, for the mathematically more sophisticated student. The problems and illustrative examples are mainly based on the materials of physical anthropology.

SIMPSON, G. G., ROE, A., and LEWONTIN, R. C.: *Quantitative Zoology.* New York, Harcourt Brace, 1960.
A work on the methodology of zoology, constituting a most attractively written introduction to the use and methodology of statistics.

SNEDECOR, G. W.: *Statistical Methods,* 4th edition. Ames, Iowa, Collegiate Press, 1948.
An excellent introduction.

Yule, G. U. and Kendall, M. G.: *An Introduction to the Theory of Statistics,* 13th edition. New York, Hafner, 1950.
A standard work, and the most commonly used by physical anthropologists, many of whom were brought up on the earlier editions of this admirable work.

WORKS ON ARCHAEOLOGY

Childe, V. G.: *A Short Introduction to Archaeology.* London, Muller, 1956.
An excellent elementary introduction to archaeology, prehistoric and recent, by one of the most distinguished archaeologists of our time.
Clark, J. G. D.: *Prehistoric Europe.* New York, Philosophical Library, 1952.
A great book on the ways in which early man maintained himself in Europe since the end of the Pleistocene Ice Age.
————: *Excavations at Starr Carr.* New York, Cambridge University Press, 1954.
A model account of an early mesolithic site in Yorkshire which, among other things, conveys not only the facts but also the feeling of what life was like in mesolithic Europe.
————: *Archaeology and Society.* Cambridge, Massachusetts, Harvard University Press, 1957.
An excellent introduction to the aims and methods of archaeology, and the reconstruction of prehistoric societies.
Cornwall, I. W.: *Bones for the Archaeologist.* London, Phoenix House, 1956.
Designed to help the archaeologist make preliminary identification of bony material. The sixteen chapters cover the identification, reconstruction, measurement, cleaning, and interpretation of bones.
Cornwall, I. W.: *Soils for the Archaeologist.* London, Phoenix House, New York, Macmillan, 1958.
A most useful work on the identification and analysis of the soils in which fossil remains and artifacts may be found.
Daniel, G. E.: *A Hundred Years of Archaeology.* New York, Macmillan, 1950.
A highly readable and informative history.
De Laet, S. J.: *Archaeology and its Problems.* New York, Macmillan, 1957.
An utterly delightful and indispensable introduction to the aims and methods of archaeology. There is not an aspect of the subject that is not covered.
De Morgan, J.: *Prehistoric Man.* New York, Knopf, 1925.
An invaluable work on the evolution of man's industries, arts, and cultures.
Heizer, R. F. (editor). *The Archaeologist at Work.* New York, Harper, 1959.
A most instructive work.
Macalister, R. A. S.: *A Textbook of European Archaeology.* Vol. I. *The Palaeolithic Period.* Cambridge: at the University Press, 1921.
Admirable even though somewhat dated. This, alas, was the only one of the projected volumes published.
MacCurdy, G. G.: *Human Origins: A Manual of Prehistory.* 2 vols. New York, Appleton, 1924.
A very complete and still useful work.
Mewhinney, H.: *A Manual for Neanderthals.* Austin, University of Texas Press, 1957.
The best book on how Stone Age man made his tools available. As the title implies it also instructs the reader how to make similar tools.

OAKLEY, K. P.: *Man the Tool Maker,* 4th edition. London, British Museum (Natural History), also Chicago, University of Chicago Press, 1958.
An admirable short work.

PIGGOTT, S.: *Approach to Archaeology.* London, Black, 1959.
A stimulating discussion of the aims and purposes of archaeology.

WILLEY, G. R.: *Method and Theory in American Archaeology.* Chicago, University of Chicago Press, 1957.
An invaluable synthesis of New World archaeology.

WORMINGTON, H. M.: *Ancient Man in North America.* 4th ed. Denver Museum of Natural History, 1957.
The best work on the archeology of North America.

ZEUNER, F. E.: *Dating the Past.* 4th ed. New York, Longmans, 1957.
The basic work on geochronology with especial reference to archeology.

FILM-MAKING FOR FIELD WORKERS AND OTHERS

For the details of technique, equipment, care, and handling of film see N. G. Dyhrenfurth, "Film making for scientific field workers," *Amer. Anthropol., 54:* 147-152, 1952.

RADIOCARBON DATING SERVICES

A publication devoted largely to the publication of radiocarbon date lists from various parts of the world, is published separately under the title *Radiocarbon Supplement,* by the *American Journal of Science,* Box 1905A, Yale Station, New Haven, Connecticut. Published annually. Subscription $2.50.

Radiocarbon Dates Association, Inc., Peabody Foundation, Box 71, Andover, Massachusetts, supplies subscribers with edge-punched cards recording specimens assayed and their radiocarbon dates.

Radiocarbon dating service is provided, on a commercial basis, by Isotopes, Inc., 123 Woodland Avenue, Westwood, New Jersey.

TABLE OF WEIGHTS AND MEASURES

1 Micron (μ) = 1 thousandth of a millimeter (mm)
1 Millimeter = 1 thousandth of a meter
10 millimeters = 1 centimeter (cm)
10 centimeters = 1 decimeter (dm)
10 decimeters = 1 meter (m)

1 meter = 10 decimeters / 100 centimeters / 1000 millimeters

1 inch = 25.4 millimeters
1 foot = 30.5 centimeters (approximately), or 0.3048 meter
5½ inches = 14.0 centimeters
1 yard = 0.9144 meter
1 centimeter = .3937 inch
1 meter = 39.37 inches
1 mile = 1.6093 kilometers
Volume = Length x Breadth x Thickness
Area = Length x Breadth
1 cubic inch = 16.387 cubic centimeters
1 cubic centimeter (c.c. or cc) = 0.061 cubic inch
1 cubic centimeter of water at 4° C. weighs 1 gram
1 liter of water at 4° C. weighs 1000 grams and is called a kilogram
1 decigram = 1/10 gram (dgm)
1 centigram = 1/100 gram (cgm)
1 milligram = 1/1000 gram (mgm)

1 cubic decimeter (cd) = (1000 cubic centimeters) = 61.024 cubic inches
1 cubic meter (100 cubic decimeters) = 35.3148 cubic feet
1 cubic decimeter = 1 liter
1 liter = 1.81 pints
4 liters = 7 pints or 112 ounces
1 pint = 16 ounces
1 ounce = 28.350 grams
1 gram = about 1/28 ounce
1 kilogram = 2 pounds 3¼ ounces
16 ounces = 1 pound
3.527 ounces = 100 grams
1 pound = 453.592 grams

DRY MEASURE

Pints	Quarts	Gallons	Cubic Inches	Metric
1	0.5	0.125	33.600	550.599 cu. millimeters
2	1.0	0.25	67.201	1.101 liters
8	4.0	1.0	268.803	4.405 liters
16	8.0	2.0	537.605	8.809 liters
64	32.0	8.0	2150.42	35.238 liters

Specific Gravity = The number of times a body or substance is heavier or lighter than an equal volume of water (or some other substance taken as a standard), under specified conditions of temperature and pressure.

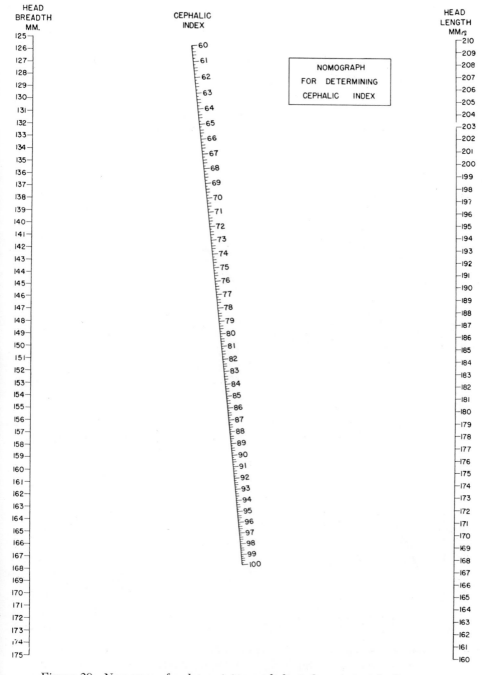

Figure 29. Nomogram for determining cephalic index. A straight line passing from the measurement for head breadth to the measurement for head length will yield the correct reading for cephalic index in the middle column. (From the *Yearbook of Physical Anthropology for 1949.* Courtesy, Dr. G. W. Lasker and the Wenner-Gren Foundation for Anthropological Research, New York.)

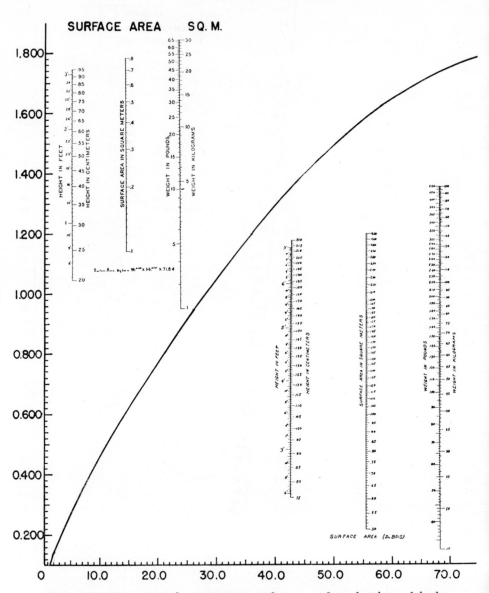

Figure 30. Nomogram for estimating surface area from height and body weight. (Surface area, Sq. Cm. = Wt.$^{0.425}$ × Ht.$^{0.725}$ × 71.84). The subject's surface area is found by drawing a straight line between the point representing his weight and the point representing his height. (From J. D. Crawford *et al.* Courtesy, *Pediatrics*.)

GENE AND GENOTYPE EQUILIBRIA, POPULA-
TIONS AND GENES, THE HARDY-
WEINBERG LAW

ONE BRANCH of genetics studies the distribution and movement of genes (gene flow) in populations. Here the geneticist and physical anthropologist have similar interests and problems. The population geneticist is concerned with all those conditions that govern gene distributions and their changes. The "conditions" refer to such factors as size of population, degree of isolation from other populations, forms of mating or marriage-regulations, differential migration (emigration and immigration), mutation, selection, and hybridization.

In the course of the history of virtually every population all these factors tend to be operative, and it is highly probable that every one of these factors, to varying extents, has contributed to the differences in gene frequencies which exist for some traits in different populations.

In the absence of the modifying conditions mentioned above, and frequently in their presence, the genetic structure of a population, that is to say the frequency distribution of its genes, tends to remain stable. The same proportions of the same genes tend to reappear generation after generation. Such a genetically stable population is said to be in *equilibrium.*

In large populations mating is usually random in respect of any particular gene, and this is what is meant when we speak of random mating—and *not* that individuals choose their mates at random, a condition that applies in no human society. The technical term for random mating is *panmixia,* a random mating population is said to be *panmictic.*

In a large panmictic population in which the pressures of mutation and selection, or other factors having similar effects upon gene frequencies, are absent or low, genotype frequencies, after the first generation of random mating, will remain indefinitely unchanged. This phenomenon is known as the Hardy-Weinberg Law (or Hardy-Weinberg Equilibrium), a law independently worked out in 1908 by the English mathematician G. H. Hardy and the German physician W. Weinberg.

In spite of three somewhat unreal assumptions, namely, infinite populations, low mutation, and little selection, the Hardy-Weinberg Law is found to work with remarkable precision in real finite populations. Not only this, it is a tool of considerable heuristic value, for when it is found not to work it may at once be suspected that we are dealing with a population in which special conditions prevail, such as isolating barriers between segments of the population which prevent free interbreeding within it. With the removal of such reproductively isolating barriers the Hardy-Weinberg Law would be found to hold true.

We shall take as a simple example of the manner in which the Hardy-Weinberg Law works a population in which there is random mating in respect of two autosomal alleles A and a. The frequencies of these alleles is 50 per cent each. Remembering that it is not phenotypes that are so much involved as the gametes, that is, the eggs and sperms, half of the eggs will carry A and half a, and so will the sperms. The results of the random combination of such eggs and sperms in the zygotes may be determined from Table XXI. From this will be seen that the frequencies of the alleles A and a remain unchanged at 50 per cent each, ¼th of the individuals will be AA, ½ Aa, and another ¼th aa.

SPERMS / EGGS	A p	a q
A p	AA p^2	Aa pq
a q	Aa pq	aa q^2

$$= p^2 AA + 2pq Aa + q^2 aa,$$
or, in the example given in the text,
$$= \tfrac{1}{4} AA + \tfrac{1}{2} Aa + \tfrac{1}{4} aa$$

Table XXI. The maintenance of genotype equilibrium. The Hardy-Weinberg Law

Matings at random between the members of this population, and the offspring of such marriages, with respect to the genes A and a, will yield 9 possible matings, and precisely the same proportions of genotypes as existed in the parental population, as shown in Table XXII.

With special exceptions the Hardy-Weinberg Law applies to all populations, however unequal the frequencies of certain genes may be. It can, therefore, be generalized in the binomial $(p + q)^2$, where p equals the frequency of A, and q equals the frequency of its allele a, and $p + q = 1$. The genotype frequencies in each generation equal

9 Possible Matings	Offspring of 9 Matings		
$\frac{1}{16} AA \times AA$	$\frac{1}{16} AA$		
$\frac{1}{8} AA \times Aa$	$\frac{1}{16} AA$	$\frac{1}{16} Aa$	
$\frac{1}{8} Aa \times AA$	$\frac{1}{16} AA$	$\frac{1}{16} Aa$	
$\frac{1}{16} AA \times aa$		$\frac{1}{16} Aa$	
$\frac{1}{4} Aa \times Aa$	$\frac{1}{16} AA$	$\frac{1}{8} Aa$	$\frac{1}{16} aa$
$\frac{1}{16} aa \times AA$		$\frac{1}{16} Aa$	
$\frac{1}{8} Aa \times aa$		$\frac{1}{16} Aa$	$\frac{1}{16} aa$
$\frac{1}{8} aa \times Aa$		$\frac{1}{16} Aa$	$\frac{1}{16} aa$
$\frac{1}{16} aa \times aa$			$\frac{1}{16} aa$

Proportion of same genotypes $\quad \frac{1}{4} AA + \frac{1}{2} Aa + \frac{1}{4} aa$

Table XXII. The proportions of genotypes in 9 possible matings of individuals with genes A and a.

$(pA + qa)^2 = p^2AA + 2pqAa + q^2aa$, which is precisely what we found in Tables XXI and XXII for the special case of $p = q = \frac{1}{2}$. A similar formula may be derived for loci with more than two alleles.

The Hardy-Weinberg Law explains how it comes about that the genotypic frequencies for such traits as brown eyes and blue eyes, for tasting and non-tasting, the blood groups, and all similar traits dependent upon contrasting alleles are likely to be maintained in the same proportions generation after generation.

It should at once be evident then, why statements to the effect that brown eyes being dominant over blue, the former must eventually swamp the latter, or that the higher frequency of brachycephaly in certain populations is due to the dominance of the alleles for this trait, are erroneous. The error committed is the assumption that the numerical frequency of any trait in a population represents a reflection of the number of dominant alleles conditioning the trait.

The fact, however, is that phenotypic frequency has no necessary relation to either the dominance or the recessiveness of alleles. Dominance and recessiveness refer only to the expression of the alleles in individuals possessing them. The frequency of any phenotype in a *population* is related to the frequency of the allele controlling it, regardless of that allele's dominance or recessiveness. There are numerous conditions in man which are due to a dominant allele, but those conditions are rare in man, simply because the dominant gene is much less frequent than its normal alternative. Examples are partial albinism, the sickle-cell trait, achondroplasia, and parietal foramina of the abnormal type.*

In the case of the alleles for tasting and non-tasting, we have already seen in Chapter VI that tasting is dependent upon a single

---

* For other examples see Ashley Montagu, *Human Heredity*, pp. 328-346.

dominant gene *T,* and non-tasting upon two recessive genes *tt.* The distribution of these genes in any population will invariably be found to follow the Hardy-Weinberg Law.

Dominant alleles in any population do not tend to replace recessive alleles. The frequency of an allele in a population is not determined by its being either dominant or recessive, but largely by the fact of its being of greater or lesser selective value.

The Hardy-Weinberg Law states that regardless of past history, random mating for one generation yields genotypic frequencies in the proportions $p^2 : 2pq : q^2$.

Gene frequency can be at equilibrium in the sense that p does not change from generation to generation in a number of circumstances, such, for example, as the following:

1. *No selection. Mutation in opposite directions.* In the absence of selection the frequency of a gene will depend upon relative rates of mutation in favorable and unfavorable directions.

2. *Selection in opposite direction from mutation.* A gene may be in process of elimination from a population, but persists within that population because the rate of elimination of the gene by selection is equal to the rate at which the gene is being reintroduced into the population by mutation.

3. *Heterozygote superior to both homozygotes.* This is well illustrated by the case of the sickle-cell trait in which the heterozygote *AS* is superior to the normal homozygote *AA* and the sickle cell anemia homozygote *SS.*

4. *Diversity of niches or environments.* If the environment is not uniform over the area occupied by a population, different genotypes may have different fitnesses in each phase of the environment. In which case polymorphism (gene equilibrium) may be preserved provided the heterozygotes are more efficient over a wider range of environments than the homozygotes.

5. *Compensation effect: more children born in families with defectives.* Where the homozygote recessive is defective, there appears to be a tendency in the families involved to have more children than normal, and more of these tend to be heterozygotes than are produced in the general population, a balanced polymorphism can be thus maintained.

6. *Dependence of fitness upon gene frequency.* When the attractiveness of blondes depends upon their rarity in the population they are at a selective advantage, and therefore increase in number. Should

blondes increase to be as common as the air, then Phoebe ceases to be esteemed fair, and is then at a selective disadvantage, and tends to decrease in frequency. At some point in this process genetic equilibrium is reached.

As another illustration of the operation of this factor reference may be made to disease. In a large population of susceptible individuals an epidemic will spread quite rapidly, and the susceptibles will be at a selective disadvantage compared to the immune individuals. However, if most of the population is immune the disease will not spread readily, and the minority (the susceptibles) will be protected by the high frequency of immunes, and equilibrium will thus be maintained.

7. *Sex differences.* If selection is different in the two sexes gene equilibrium may be achieved. For example, in a population in which fat women are preferred to svelte ones, and lithe men are preferred to somewhat over-upholstered ones, a balanced polymorphism for both sexes will be reached.

"ETHNIC GROUP" AND "RACE"

In the Unesco Statement on Race paragraph 6 reads as follows: "National, religious, geographic, linguistic and cultural groups do not necessarily coincide with racial groups; and the cultural traits of such groups have no demonstrated connection with racial traits. Because serious errors of this kind are habitually committed when the term 'race' is used in popular parlance, it would be better when speaking of human races to drop the term 'race' altogether and speak of *ethnic groups.*" It should be noted that there is a clear acknowledgment of the existence of human races in this paragraph, and that the emphasis is on popular parlance. It is recommended that in the universe of popular parlance the term "race" be dropped altogether and that we speak of "ethnic groups." Since races in various biological senses of the word can be conceived to exist in man, it would seem unnecessary to drop this long-established term in favor of some other. The truth, however, is that there are so many different senses in which even biologists use the term, that many leading members of that profession prefer not to use it at all. Huxley a biologist and Haddon a physical anthropologist repudiated the term in 1936.[1] Calman recommended that the term "variety" should be avoided altogether and suggested that "Other terms such as 'geographical race,' 'form,' 'phase,' and so forth, may be useful in particular instances but are better not used until some measure of agreement is reached as to their precise meaning."[2] Kalmus writes: "A very important term which was originally used in systematics is 'race.' Nowadays, however, its use is avoided as far as possible in genetics."[3] In a more recent work Kalmus writes, "It is customary to discuss the local varieties of humanity in terms of 'race.' However, it is unnecessary to use this greatly debased word, since it is easy to describe populations without it."[3a] G. S. Carter, in his book on *Animal Evolution*, writes that

---

[1] Huxley and Haddon, *We Europeans,* pp. 82-83.

[2] Calman, *The Classification of Animals,* p. 14.

[3] Kalmus, *Genetics,* p. 45.

[3a] Kalmus, *Heredity and Variation,* p. 30.

the terms "'race,' 'variety,' and 'form' are used so loosely and in so many senses that it is advisable to avoid using them as infraspecific categories."[4] Professor Ernst Hanhart denies that there are any "true races" in man,[5] and Professor L. S. Penrose, in a review of Dunn and Dobzhansky's little book *Heredity, Race and Society,* writes that he is unable to "see the necessity for the rather apologetic retention of the obsolete term 'race,' when what is meant is simply a given population differentiated by some social, geographical or genetical character, or . . . merely by a gene frequency peculiarity. The use of the almost mystical concept of race makes the presentation of the facts about the geographical and linguistic groups . . . unnecessarily complicated."[6]

In spite of these strictures many biologists will continue to use the term, and if they can use it in an adequately defined manner so that their meaning can be clearly understood by other scientists, erroneous though that usage may be, it will be all the more easy for the critic to direct attention to the sources of the error. It cannot be too frequently emphasized that definitions are not to be achieved at the beginning of an inquiry but only at the end of one. Such inquiries have not yet been completed to the satisfaction of most scientists who have paid considered attention to the subject of 'race.' The term, therefore, at best is at the present time not really allowable on any score in man. One may or may not be of the opinion that the term "race" ought to be dropped altogether from the vocabulary, because it is so prematurely defined and confusing and because biologists and other scientists are frequently guilty of using it incorrectly, and that therefore it would be better if they did not lend the aura of their authority to the use of so confusing a word. The term "subspecies" has been used as the equivalent of the term "race," but this suffers from the same disadvantages, and has been as misused as its equivalent.[7] The term "race" is so embarrassed by confused and mystical meanings, and has so many blots upon its escutcheon, that a discouragement of its use would constitute an encouragement to clearer thinking.

In opposition to this view a number of objections have been expressed. One doesn't change anything by changing names. It's an artful dodge. Why not meet the problem head-on? If, in popular

---

[4] Carter, *Animal Evolution,* p. 163.

[5] Hanhart, in A. Sorsby, *Clinical Genetics,* p. 545.

[6] Penrose, *Annals of Eugenics,* 17:252, 1952.

[7] Hall, Zoological subspecies of man at the peace table. *J. Mammal.,* 27:358-364, 1946.

usage, the term "race" has been befogged and befouled, why not cleanse it of the smog and foulness and restore it to its pristine condition? Re-education should be attempted by establishing the true meaning of "race," not by denying its existence. One cannot combat racism by enclosing the word in quotes. It is not the word that requires changing but people's ideas about it. It is a common failing to argue from the abuse of an idea to its total exclusion. And so on.

It was Francis Bacon who remarked that truth grows more readily out of error than it does out of confusion. The time may come when it may be possible for most men to use the term "race" in a legitimate scientific sense, with clarity and with reason. But that time is not yet. It does not appear to be generally realized that while high walls do not a prison make, scientific terms are capable of doing so. Until people are soundly educated to understand the muddlement of ideas which is represented by such terms as "race" they will continue to believe in absurdities. And as Voltaire so acutely remarked, "As long as people believe in absurdities they will continue to commit atrocities." Words are what men breathe into them. Men have a strong tendency to use words and phrases which cloak the unknown in the undefined or undefinable. As Housman put it, "calling in ambiguity of language to promote confusion of thought." [8]

The layman's conception of "race" is so confused and emotionally muddled that any attempt to modify it would seem to be met by the greatest obstacle of all, the term "race" itself. This is another reason why the attempt to retain the term "race" in popular parlance must fail. The term is a trigger word; utter it and a whole series of emotionally conditioned responses follow. The phrase "ethnic group" suffers from no such defect. If we are to clarify the minds of those who think in terms of "race" we must cease using the word primarily because in the layman's mind the term defines conditions which do not in fact exist. There is no such thing as the kind of "race" in which the layman believes. If we are to re-educate him in a sound conception of the meaning of that population or somatological or genetic group which we prefer to designate by the general and non-committal phrase *ethnic group,* then it would seem far more reasonable to convey to him the temporariness of the situation with a general rather than with a particular term. This is particularly desirable when it is sought to remove a prevailing erroneous conception and substitute one that clarifies without solidifying. Professor Henry Sigerist has well said that "it is never sound to continue the use of terminology with

[8] Housman, *The Name and Nature of Poetry,* p. 31.

which the minds of millions of people have been poisoned even when the old terms are given new meanings." [9] And Professor George Gaylord Simpson has written, "A word for which everyone has a different definition, usually unstated, ceases to serve the function of communication and its use results in futile arguments about nothing. There is also a sort of Gresham's Law for words; redefine them as we will, their worst or most extreme meaning is almost certain to remain current and to tend to drive out the meaning we might prefer." [10] Bertrand Russell has suggested that for words that have strong emotional overtones we should substitute in our arguments the letters of the alphabet.

The biologist who has been largely concerned with the study of animal populations will be likely to take an oversimplified view of the problems here involved and to dismiss such attempts at re-education of the layman as unsatisfactory. By substituting one term for another, he will say, one solves nothing. It it quite as possible to feel "ethnic group prejudice" as it is to feel "race prejudice." Perhaps. But this kind of comment indicates that the real point has been missed. The phrase "ethnic group" is *not* a substitute for the term "race." The grounds upon which it is suggested constitute a fundamental difference in viewpoint which significantly differentiates what the phrase stands for from what the term stands for. It is not a question of changing names, and there is no question of resorting to devices or artful dodges—the imputation would be silly. If what the phrase "ethnic group" means is clearly understood and accepted, "ethnic group prejudice" would hardly require to be taken seriously. There have been some who have felt that the use of the phrase "ethnic group" was an avoidance of the main issue. On the other hand, most students of human nature would take the view that such a usage constitutes a more realistic and more promising approach to the problem of lay thinking on this subject than the method of attempting to put new meaning into the old bottle of "race." I agree with Korzybski that "because of the great semantic influence of the structure of language on the masses of mankind, leading, as it does, through lack of better understanding and *evaluation* to *speculation on terms*, it seems advisable to abandon completely terms which imply to the *many* the suggested elementalism, although these terms are used in a proper non-elementalistic way by the few." [11]

---

[9] Sigerist, *A History of Medicine*, p. 101.

[10] Simpson, *The Major Features of Evolution*, p. 268.

[11] Korzybski, *Science and Sanity*, p. 31.

The ground on which the phrase "ethnic group" is principally suggested is that it is easier to re-educate people by introducing a new conception with a new distinctive term, particularly, I repeat, when it is desired to remove a prevailing erroneous conception and introduce a new and more correct one. Those who do not understand that the greatest obstacle to the process of re-education would be the retention of the old term "race," a term which enshrines the errors it is desired to remove, do not understand the deep implicit meanings which this word has inescapably come to possess for so many of its users. The question may, then, be asked: Will the phrase "ethnic group" be sufficient to cause such persons to alter their ideas? The answer is for some "No," for others, "It will help"; and for still others, "Yes." No one should be so naïve as to suppose that by this means alone one is going to solve the "race" problem! The suggestions here made are calculated to help; they can do no more at best. Each time one uses the term "race" most individuals believe they understand what is meant, when in fact the chances are that what they understand by the term is largely false. "Race" is something so familiar that in speaking of it one takes one's private meaning completely for granted and one never thinks to question it. On the other hand, when one uses the phrase "ethnic group" wherever "race" would have been used, the question is generally asked: "What do you mean by 'ethnic group'?" And that at once affords the opportunity to discuss the facts and explain their meaning as well as the falsities of the prevailing conception of "race." This, it seems to me, is one of the greatest educational advantages of the phrase "ethnic group" over the term "race." Another advantage of the phrase is that it leaves all question of definition open, it refers specifically to human populations which are believed to exhibit a certain degree, amount, or frequency of un-determined physical likenesses or homogeneity. An ethnic group has already been described as one of a number of populations, which populations together comprise the species *Homo sapiens,* and which individually maintain their differences, physical and cultural, by means of isolating mechanisms such as geographic and social barriers. These differences vary as the power of the geographic and social barriers vary. Where these barriers are of high power, such ethnic groups will tend to remain distinct from each other geographically or ecologically.

English and English write as follows, "Ethnic group is an intentionally vague or general term used to avoid some of the difficulties of *race.* The ethnic group may be a nation, a people (such as the Jews), a language group (the Dakota Indians), a sociologically defined so-called race (the American Negro), or a group bound together in a coherent cultural entity by a religion (the Amish)." [12] To which one may add that the group may be characterized by a certain unity of genetic or physical traits.

Yet another advantage of the phrase "ethnic group" is that it avoids the reductionist or "nothing but" fallacy, that is to say, the notion that men are nothing but the resultant of their biological heredity, that they are what they are because of their genes. The phrase "ethnic group" is calculated to provide the necessary corrective to this erroneous viewpoint by eliminating the question-begging emphases of the biologistic bias on purely physical factors and differences, and demanding that the question of definition be left open until the necessary scientific research and answers are available. The emphasis is shifted to the fact that man is a uniquely cultural creature as well as a physical organism, and that under the influence of human culture the plasticity of man, both mentally and physically, is greatly increased—indeed, to such an extent as to lead anthropologists to the creation of races upon the basis of physical traits which were subsequently discovered to be due to cultural factors, as, for example, the head forms of the so-called Armenoid and Dinaric "races."

Here, too, reply may be made to those who may object that the phrase "ethnic group" is too reminiscent of the cultural. But this is precisely why the phrase is so well found. The Greek word *ethnos* originally meant a number of people living together, and subsequently came to be used in the sense of a tribe, group, nation, or people. In modern times the term "ethnic" has occasionally been used to refer to a group identified by ties both of race and of nationality. This is pretty much what the phrase "ethnic group" ought to be taken to mean in the sense given in our description of an "ethnic group."

If it be said that what the student of man's variety is interested in is the way in which human groups came to be what they are, and that for this reason it is the biological facts and mechanisms in which he must be chiefly interested, the answer must be made that anyone who believes this must be disabused of his belief as quickly as possible. For it must be emphasized again that man is not merely a physical organism but a *human* being who as a member of a cultural group has been greatly influenced by his culture. Human populations have had a remarkable assortment of marriage or breeding regulations, for

---

[12] English and English, *A Comprehensive Dictionary of Psychological and Psychoanalytical Terms,* 189.

instance, varying standards of sexual selection, different kinds of social barriers, mobility, and similar variables, all of which have probably played an appreciable part in the evolution of ethnic differences. These are the very kinds of factors which are most neglected by those who come to the study of man with a biologistic bias. It would for such students of man, especially those who come in from the non-human biological fields, as well as for the layman, be a great advantage to be required to look at the problem of human variety from the viewpoint of the "ethnic group" rather than from that of "race." Where man is concerned the biologist, like the layman, needs to add a cultural dimension to his horizons. This is what the phrase "ethnic group" will help him to do.

The conception of an "ethnic group" is quite different from that which is associated with the term "race." The phrase "ethnic group" represents a different way of looking at populations, an open, non-question-begging way, a tentative, noncommittal, experimental way, based on the new understanding which the sciences of genetics and anthropology have made possible. A term is discontinued, retired, but another is not merely substituted for it; rather a new conception of human populations is introduced replacing the old one, which is now dropped, and a term or phrase suitable to this new conception is suggested. The old conception is *not* retained and a new name given to it, but a new conception is introduced under its own name. That is a very different thing from a mere change in names. It is important to be quite clear upon this point, for the *new conception* embraced in the phrase "ethnic group" renders the possibility of the development of "ethnic group prejudice" quite impossible, for as soon as the nature of this conception is understood it cancels the possibility of any such development. It is a noncontaminating neutral concept.

Perhaps the greatest advantage of the phrase "ethnic group" is that it is noncommittal and somewhat flexible. It may be applied to any group concerning which physical and cultural traits are so identified that it is given a certain distinctiveness which appears to separate it from other groups. The phrase may also be used as embracing the definition of race in the biological sense, and particularly groups which are less clearly defined, which may or may not be races and hence should not be called races in the absence of the necessary scientific demonstration. All that we say when we use the phrase "ethnic group" is that here is a group of people who physically, and distinct group. Until we know what it really is, and until we perhaps in other additional ways, may be regarded as a more or less understand thoroughly what we are talking about with respect to this and all other groups, let us call all such groups "ethnic groups." In other words, the concept of "ethnic group" implies a question mark, *not* a period. It implies that many questions remain to be asked, and that many answers will have to be given before we can say precisely what any particular ethnic group represents.

To conclude and summarize: The advantages of the phrase "ethnic group" are: first, while emphasizing the fact that one is dealing with a distinguishable group, this noncommittal phrase leaves the whole question of the precise status of the group on physical and other grounds open for further discussion and research; second, it recognizes the fact that it is a group which has been subject to the action of cultural influences; and third, it eliminates all obfuscating emotional implications.

As for the suggested dropping or the restricted or suspended use of the term "race," there are many parallels for this in science. Possibly the most striking one in recent years is the dropping of the term "instinct" by psychologists for similar reasons to those which make the term "race" undesirable.[13] Similarly, in anthropology the term "savage" has been completely dropped, while the term "primitive" as referring to living peoples is largely being abandoned in favor of the term "nonliterate" for much the same reason, namely, the inaccuracy of the earlier terms, and hence their unsuitability. In biology the term "unit character" as erroneously referring to single genes as determining single characters or traits, has been for ever banished from the scientific vocabulary. Retardative concepts like "phlogiston" of eighteenth-century chemistry have been dropped never to be re-adopted. It may be that the terms "instinct" and "race" may someday be shown to have more than a merely verbal validity, but until that time it would be more in accordance with the scientific spirit to declare a moratorium on the use of the term "race."

The phrase "ethnic group" serves as a challenge to thought and as a stimulus to rethink the foundations of one's beliefs. It encourages the passage from ignorant certainty to thoughtful uncertainty. For the layman, as for others, the term "race" closes the door on his understanding; the phrase "ethnic group" opens it.

---

[13] See Bernard, *Instinct: A Study in Social Psychology.*

The UNESCO Statements on Race

Two STATEMENTS on Race were issued by UNESCO. The first was largely the work of a group of social scientists, the second was the product of a group of physical anthropologists and geneticists. The first statement was published on 18 July 1950 under the title "The UNESCO Statement by Experts on Race Problems," and the second was published July 15, 1952 under the title "Statement on the Nature of Race and Race Differences—by Physical Anthropologists and Geneticists, September 1952." In conversation one would refer to the first as "The Statement on Race" and to the second as "Statement on the Nature of Race." As the reader will perceive, there is marked agreement between the social and the natural scientists.

Most of the members on the first committee would, I believe, now replace the term "Division" in the first Statement with the term "Major Group" from the second Statement.

UNESCO Statement on Race—By Social Scientists, July 1950

1. Scientists have reached general agreement in recognizing that mankind is one: that all men belong to the same species, *Homo sapiens*. It is further generally agreed among scientists that all men are probably derived from the same common stock; and that such differences as exist between different groups of mankind are due to the operation of evolutionary factors of differentiation such as isolation, the drift and random fixation of the material particles which control heredity (the genes), changes in the structure of these particles, hybridization, and natural selection. In these ways groups have arisen of varying stability and degree of differentiation which have been classified in different ways for different purposes.

2. From the biological standpoint, the species *Homo sapiens* is made up of a number of populations, each one of which differs from the others in the frequency of one or more genes. Such genes, responsible for the hereditary differences between men, are always few when compared to the whole genetic constitution of man and to the vast number of genes common to all human beings regardless of the

148

population to which they belong. This means that the likenesses among men are far greater than their differences.

3. A race, from the biological standpoint, may therefore be defined as one of the group of populations constituting the species *Homo sapiens*. These populations are capable of inter-breeding with one another but, by virtue of the isolating barriers which in the past kept them more or less separated, exhibit certain physical differences as a result of their somewhat different biological histories. These represent variations, as it were, on a common theme.

4. In short, the term "race" designates a group or population characterized by some concentrations, relative as to frequency and distribution, of hereditary particles (genes) or physical characters, which appear, fluctuate, and often disappear in the course of time by reason of geographic and/or cultural isolation. The varying manifestations of these traits in different populations are perceived in different ways by each group. What is perceived is largely preconceived, so that each group arbitrarily tends to misinterpret the variability which occurs as a fundamental difference which separates that group from all others.

5. These are the scientific facts. Unfortunately, however, when most people use the term "race" they do not do so in the sense above defined. To most people, a race is any group of people whom they choose to describe as a race. Thus, many national, religious, geographic, linguistic or cultural groups have, in such loose usage, been called a "race," when obviously Americans are not a race, nor are Englishmen, nor Frenchmen, nor any other national group. Catholics, Protestants, Moslems, and Jews are not races, nor are groups who speak English or any other language thereby definable as a race, people who live in Iceland or England or India are not races; nor are people who are culturally Turkish or Chinese, or the like thereby describable as races.

6. National, religious, geographic, linguistic and cultural groups do not necessarily coincide with racial groups; and the cultural traits of such groups have no demonstrated genetic connection with racial traits. Because serious errors of this kind are habitually committed when the term "race" is used in popular parlance, it would be better when speaking of human races to drop the term "race" altogether and speak of *ethnic groups*.

7. Now what has the scientist to say about the groups of mankind which may be recognized at the present time? Human races can be

and have been differently classified by different anthropologists, but at the present time most anthropologists agree in classifying the greater part of present-day mankind into three major divisions, as follows:

> The Mongoloid Division
> The Negroid Division
> The Caucasoid Division

The biological processes which the classifier has here embalmed, as it were, are dynamic, not static. These divisions were not the same in the past as they are at present, and there is every reason to believe that they will change in the future.

8. Many sub-groups or ethnic groups within these divisions have been described. There is no general agreement upon their number, and in any event most ethnic groups have not yet been either studied or described by the physical anthropologists.

9. Whatever classification the anthropologist makes of man, he never includes mental characteristics as part of those classifications. It is now generally recognized that intelligence tests do not in themselves enable us to differentiate safely between what is due to innate capacity and what is the result of environmental influences, training and education. Wherever it has been possible to make allowances for differences in environmental opportunities, the tests have shown essential similarity in mental characters among all human groups. In short, given similar degrees of cultural opportunity to realize their potentialities, the average achievement of the members of each ethnic group is about the same. The scientific investigations of recent years fully support the dictum of Confucius (551-478 B.C.) "Men's natures are alike; it is their habits that carry them far apart."

10. The scientific material available to us at present does not justify the conclusion that inherited genetic differences are a major factor in producing the differences between the cultures and cultural achievements of different peoples or groups. It does indicate, however, that the history of the cultural experience which each group has undergone is the major factor in explaining such differences. The one trait which above all others has been at a premium in the evolution of men's mental characters has been educability, plasticity. This is a trait which all human beings possess. It is indeed, a species character of *Homo sapiens*.

11. So far as temperament is concerned, there is no definite evidence that there exist inborn differences between human groups. There is evidence that whatever group differences of the kind there might

be are greatly over-ridden by the individual differences, and by the differences springing from environmental factors.

12. As for personality and character, these may be considered raceless. In every human group a rich variety of personality and character types will be found, and there is no reason for believing that any human group is richer than any other in these respects.

13. With respect to race-mixture, the evidence points unequivocally to the fact that this has been going on from the earliest times. Indeed, one of the chief processes of race-formation and race-extinction or absorption is by means of hybridization between races or ethnic groups. Furthermore, no convincing evidence has been adduced that race-mixture of itself produces biologically bad effects. Statements that human hybrids frequently show undesirable traits, both physically and mentally, physical disharmonies and mental degeneracies, are not supported by the facts. There is, therefore, no *biological* justification for prohibiting intermarriage between persons of different ethnic groups.

14. The biological fact of race and the myth of "race" should be distinguished, for all practical social purposes "race" is not so much a biological phenomenon as a social myth. The myth of "race" has created an enormous amount of human and social damage. In recent years it has taken a heavy toll in human lives and caused untold suffering. It still prevents the normal development of millions of human beings and deprives civilization of the effective co-operation of productive minds. The biological differences between ethnic groups should be disregarded from the standpoint of social acceptance and social action. The unity of mankind from both the biological and social viewpoints is the main thing. To recognize this and to act accordingly is the first requirement of modern man. It is but to recognize what a great biologist wrote in 1875: "As man advances in civilization, and small tribes are united into larger communities, the simplest reason would tell each individual that he ought to extend his social instincts and sympathies to all the members of the same nation, though personally unknown to him. This point being once reached, there is only an artificial barrier to prevent his sympathies extending to the men of all nations and races." These are the words of Charles Darwin in *The Descent of Man* (2nd ed., 1875, pp. 187-188). And, indeed, the whole of human history shows that a co-operative spirit is not only natural to men, but more deeply rooted than any self-seeking tendencies. If this were not so we should not see the growth of integration and organization of his communities which the centuries and the millennia plainly exhibit.

15. We now have to consider the bearing of these statements on the problem of human equality. It must be asserted with the utmost emphasis that equality as an ethical principle in no way depends upon the assertion that human beings are in fact equal in endowment. Obviously individuals in all ethnic groups vary greatly among themselves in endowment. Nevertheless, the characteristics in which human groups differ from one another are often exaggerated and used as a basis for questioning the validity of equality in the ethical sense. For this purpose we have thought it worth while to set out in a formal manner what is at present scientifically established concerning individual and group differences.

(1) In matters of race, the only characteristics which anthropologists can effectively use as a basis for classifications are physical and physiological.

(2) According to present knowledge there is no proof that the groups of mankind differ in their innate mental characteristics, whether in respect to intelligence or temperament. The scientific evidence indicates that the range of mental capacities in all ethnic groups is much the same.

(3) Historical and sociological studies support the view that genetic differences are not of importance in determining the social and cultural differences between different groups of *Homo sapiens,* and that the social and cultural *changes* in different groups have, in the main, been independent of *changes* in inborn constitution. Vast social changes have occurred which were not in any way connected with changes in racial type.

(4) There is no evidence that race mixture as such produces bad results from the biological point of view. The social results of race mixture whether for good or ill are to be traced to social factors.

(5) All normal human beings are capable of learning to share in a common life, to understand the nature of mutual service and reciprocity, and to respect social obligations and contracts. Such biological differences as exist between members of different ethnic groups have no relevance to problems of social and political organization, moral life and communication between human beings.

Lastly, biological studies lend support to the ethic of universal brotherhood; for man is born with drives toward co-operation, and unless those drives are satisfied, men and nations alike fall ill. Man is born a social being who can reach his fullest development only through interaction with his fellows. The denial at any point of this social bond between men and man brings with it disintegration.

In this sense, every man is his brother's keeper. For every man is a piece of the continent, a part of the main, because he is involved in mankind.

Original statement drafted at Unesco House, Paris, by the following experts:

> Professor Ernest Beaglehole, *New Zealand.*
> Professor Juan Comas, *Mexico.*
> Professor L. A. Costa Pinto, *Brazil.*
> Professor Franklin Frazier, *United States.*
> Professor Morris Ginsberg, *United Kingdom.*
> Dr. Humayun Kabir, *India.*
> Professor Claude Levi-Strauss, *France.*
> Professor Ashley Montagu, *United States* (Rapporteur).

Text revised by Professor Ashley Montagu, after criticisms submitted by Professors Hadley Cantril, E. G. Conklin, Gunnar Dahlberg, Theodosius Dobzhansky, L. C. Dunn, Donald Hager, Julian S. Huxley, Otto Klineberg, Wilbert Moore, H. J. Muller, Gunnar Myrdal, Joseph Needham.

Statement on the Nature of Race and Race Differences by Physical Anthropologists and Geneticists
September 1952

1. Scientists are generally agreed that all men living today belong to a single species, *Homo sapiens,* and are derived from a common stock, even though there is some dispute as to when and how different human groups diverged from this common stock.

The concept of race is unanimously regarded by anthropologists as a classificatory device providing a zoological frame within which the various groups of mankind may be arranged and by means of which studies of evolutionary processes can be facilitated. In its anthropological sense, the word "race" should be reserved for groups of mankind possessing well-developed and primarily heritable physical differences from other groups. Many populations can be so classified but, because of the complexity of human history, there are also many populations which cannot easily be fitted into a racial classification.

2. Some of the physical differences between human groups are due to differences in hereditary constitution and some to differences in the environments in which they have been brought up. In most cases, both influences have been at work. The science of genetics suggests that the hereditary differences among populations of a single

species are the results of the action of two sets of processes. On the one hand, the genetic composition of isolated populations is constantly but gradually being altered by natural selection and by occasional changes (mutations) in the material particles (genes) which control heredity. Populations are also affected by fortuitous changes in gene frequency and by marriage customs. On the other hand, crossing is constantly breaking down the differentiations so set up. The new mixed populations, in so far as they, in turn, become isolated, are subject to the same processes, and these may lead to further changes. Existing races are merely the result, considered at a particular moment in time, of the total effect of such processes on the human species. The hereditary characters to be used in the classification of human groups, the limits of their variation within these groups, and thus the extent of the classificatory sub-divisions adopted may legitimately differ according to the scientific purpose in view.

3. National, religious, geographical, linguistic and cultural groups do not necessarily coincide with racial groups; and the cultural traits of such groups have no demonstrated connection with racial traits. Americans are not a race, nor are Frenchmen, nor Germans; nor *ipso facto* is any other national group. Moslems and Jews are no more races than are Roman Catholics and Protestants; nor are people who live in Iceland or Britain or India, or who speak English or any other language, or who are culturally Turkish or Chinese and the like, thereby describable as races. The use of the term "race" in speaking of such groups may be a serious error, but is one which is habitually committed.

4. Human races can be, and have been classified in different ways by different anthropologists. Most of them agree in classifying the greater part of existing mankind into at least three large units, which may be called major groups (in French *grand races,* in German *Hauptrassen*). Such a classification does not depend on any single physical character, nor does, for example, skin colour by itself necessarily distinguish one major group from another. Furthermore, so far as it has been possible to analyze them, the differences in physical structure which distinguish one major group from another give no support to popular notions of any general "superiority" or "inferiority" which are sometimes implied in referring to these groups.

Broadly speaking, individuals belonging to different major groups of mankind are distinguishable by virtue of their physical characters, but individual members, or small groups, belonging to different races within the same major group are usually not so distinguishable. Even the major groups grade into each other, and the physical traits by which they and the races within them are characterized overlap considerably. With respect to most, if not all, measurable characters, the differences among individuals belonging to the same race are greater than the differences that occur between the observed averages for two or more races within the same major group.

5. Most anthropologists do not include mental characteristics in their classification of human races. Studies within a single race have shown that both innate capacity and environmental opportunity determine the results of tests of intelligence and temperament, though their relative importance is disputed.

When intelligence tests, even non-verbal, are made on a group of non-literate people, their scores are usually lower than those of more civilized people. It has been recorded that different groups of the same race occupying similarly high levels of civilization may yield considerable differences in intelligence tests. When, however, the two groups have been brought up from childhood in similar environments, the differences are usually very slight. Moreover, there is good evidence that, given similar opportunities, the average performance (that is to say, the performance of the individual who is representative because he is surpassed by as many as he surpasses), and the variation round it, do not differ appreciably from one race to another.

Even those psychologists who claim to have found the greatest differences in intelligence between groups of different racial origin, and have contended that they are hereditary, always report that some members of the group of inferior performance surpass not merely the lowest ranking member of the superior group, but also the average of its members. In any case, it has never been possible to separate members of two groups on the basis of mental capacity, as they can often be separated on a basis of religion, skin colour, hair form or language. It is possible, though not proved, that some types of innate capacity for intellectual and emotional responses are commoner in one human group than in another, but it is certain that, within a single group, innate capacities vary as much as, if not more than, they do between different groups.

The study of the heredity of psychological characteristics is beset with difficulties. We know that certain mental diseases and defects are transmitted from one generation to the next, but we are less familiar with the part played by heredity in the mental life of normal individuals. The normal individual, irrespective of race, is essentially educable. It follows that his intellectual and moral life is largely conditioned by his training and by his physical and social environment.

It often happens that a national group may appear to be characterized by particular psychological attributes. The superficial view would be that this is due to race. Scientifically, however, we realize that any common psychological attribute is more likely to be due to a common historical and social background, and that such attributes may obscure the fact that, within different populations consisting of many human types, one will find approximately the same range of temperament and intelligence.

6. The scientific material available to us at present does not justify the conclusion that inherited genetic differences are a major factor in producing the differences between the cultures and cultural achievements of different peoples or groups. It does indicate, on the contrary, that a major factor in explaining such differences is the cultural experience which each group has undergone.

7. There is no evidence for the existence of so-called "pure" races. Skeletal remains provide the basis of our limited knowledge about earlier races. In regard to race mixture, the evidence points to the fact that human hybridization has been going on for an indefinite but considerable time. Indeed, one of the processes of race formation and race extinction or absorption is by means of hybridization between races. As there is no reliable evidence that disadvantageous effects are produced thereby, no biological justification exists for prohibiting intermarriage between persons of different races.

8. We now have to consider the bearing of these statements on the problem of human equality. We wish to emphasize that equality of opportunity and equality in law in no way depend, as ethical principles, upon the assertion that human beings are in fact equal in endowment.

9. We have thought it worth while to set out in a formal manner what is at present scientifically established concerning individual and group differences.

(1) In matters of race, the only characteristics which anthropologists have so far been able to use effectively as a basis for classification are physical (anatomical and physiological).

(2) Available scientific knowledge provides no basis for believing that the groups of mankind differ in their innate capacity for intellectual and emotional development.

(3) Some biological differences between human beings within a single race may be as great or greater than the same biological differences between races.

(4) Vast social changes have occurred that have not been connected in any way with changes in racial type. Historical and sociological studies thus support the view that genetic differences are of little significance in determining the social and cultural differences between different groups of men.

(5) There is no evidence that race mixture produces disadvantageous results from a biological point of view. The social results of race mixture whether for good or ill, can generally be traced to social factors.

(Text drafted, at Unesco House, Paris, on June 8, 1951, by: Professor R. A. M. Bergman, Royal Tropical Institute, Netherlands Anthropological Society, Amsterdam; Professor Gunnar Dahlberg, Director, State Institute for Human Genetics and Race Biology, University of Uppsala; Professor L. C. Dunn, Department of Zoology, Columbia University, New York; Professor J. B. S. Haldane, Head, Department of Biometry, University College, London; Professor M. F. Ashley Montagu, Chairman, Department of Anthropology, Rutgers University, New Brunswick, N.J.; Dr. A. E. Mourant, Director, Blood Group Reference Laboratory, Lister Institute, London; Professor Hans Nachtsheim, Director, Institut für Genetik, Freie Universität, Berlin; Dr. Eugène Schreider, Directeur adjoint du Laboratoire d'Anthropologie Physique de l'Ecole des Hautes Etudes, Paris; Professor Harry L. Shapiro, Chairman, Department of Anthropology, American Museum of Natural History, New York; Dr. J. C. Trevor, Faculty of Archaeology and Anthropology, University of Cambridge; Dr. Henri V. Vallois, Professeur au Museum d'Histoire Naturelle, Directeur du Musée, de l'Homme, Paris; Professor S. Zuckerman, Head, Department of Anatomy, Medical School, University of Birmingham. Professor Th. Dobzhansky, Department of Zoology, Columbia University, New York, and Dr. Julian Huxley contributed to the final wording.)

BIBLIOGRAPHY

ABBIE, A. A.: A new approach to the problem of human evolution. *Trans. Roy. Soc. S. Australia*, 75:70-88, 1952.

A new outlook on physical anthropology. *N.Z. Assoc. Adv. Sci.*, 28:52-63, 1951.

————: The Australian aborigine. *Oceania*, 22:91-100, 1951.

————: The original Australians. *The Leech*, 28:120-130, 1958.

————: Timing in human evolution. *Proc. Linn. Soc. New S. Wales*, 83:197-213, 1958.

ALIMEN, H.: *The Prehistory of Africa.* London, Hutchinson, 1959.

ALLEE, WARDER C.: Biology and international relations. *The New Republic*, 112:816-817, 1945.

————: *Cooperation Among Animals.* New York, Schuman, 1951.

————: Where angels fear to tread. A contribution from General Sociology to Human Ethics. *Science*, 97:518-525, 1943.

————: *Animal Aggregations.* Chicago, Univ. Chicago Press, 1931.

————, PARK, O., EMERSON, A. E., PARK, T. and SCHMIDT, K. P.: *Principles of Animal Ecology.* Philadelphia, Saunders, 1949.

ALLEN, F.: Inheritance of the Diego (Di^a) blood group factor. *Am. J. Hum. Genetics*, 10:64-67, 1958.

ALLISON, A. C.: Protection afforded by the sickle-cell trait against subtertian malarial infection. *Brit. M. J.*, I:290-294, 1954.

———— and NEVANLINNA, H. R.: Taste deficiency in Lappish and Finnish populations. *Ann. Eug.*, 17:113-114, 1952.

ALLISON, A. C., BLUMBERG, B. S. and W. A. REES: Haptoglobin types in British, Spanish Basque and Nigerian African populations. *Nature*, 181:824, 1958.

ANDREWARTHA, H. G. and BIRCH, L. C.: *The Distribution and Abundance of Animals.* Univ. Chicago Press, 1954.

ANGEL, J. L.: Constitution in female obesity. *Am. J. Phys. Anthropol.*, n.s. 7:433-471, 1949.

ARAMBOURG, C.: A recent discovery in human paleontology: Atlanthropus of Ternifine (Algeria). *Am. J. Phys. Anthropol.*, n.s. 13:191-201, 1955.

———— and BIBERSON, P.: The fossil human remains from the paleolithic of Sidi Abderrahman (Morocco). *Am. J. Phys. Anthropol.*, n.s. 14:467-489, 1956.

ARKIN, H. and COLTON, R. R.: Statistical Methods, 4th edition. New York, Barnes & Noble, 1956.

BARNES, H. E. and TEETERS, N. K.: *New Horizons in Criminology.* New York, Prentice-Hall, 1943.

BARNICOT, N. A.: Taste deficiency for phenythiourea in African Negroes and Chinese. *Ann. Eug.*, 15:248-254, 1950.

————: Human Pigmentation. *Man*, No. 144, 1957, 1-7.

————: Genetics and human races. *The New Scientist*, January 8, 1959.

BARTH, F.: On the relationships of early primates. *Am. J. Phys. Anthropol.*, n.s. 8:139-149, 1950.

BARTHOLOMEW, G. A. and BIRDSELL, J. B.: Ecology and the protohominids. *Am. Anthropol.*, 55:481-498, 1953.

BATTAGLIA, R.: Osso occipitale umano rinvenuto nel giacimento pleistocenico di Quinzano nel Comune di Verona. *Palaeontographica Italica*, 42:1-31, 1948.

BENDER, M. A., and METTLER, L. E.: Chromosome studies on primates. *Science*, 128:186-190, 1958.

BENDYSHE, T: The history of anthropology. *Mem. Anthropol. Soc. London*, 1:335, 1863; 1864.

BENEDICT, R.: *Race: Science and Politics.* New York, Viking Press, 1959.

BERRILL, N. J.: *Man's Emerging Mind.* New York, Dodd Mead, 1955.

BEWS, J. W.: *Human Ecology.* New York, Oxford, 1935.

BINGHAM, H. C.: *Gorillas in a Native Habitat.* Washington, D.C., Carnegie Inst., Pub. No. 426, 1932.

BIRD, G. W. G., et al.: The blood groups and hemoglobin of the Ghorkhas of Nepal. *Am. J. Phys. Anthropol.*, n.s. 15:163-169, 1957.

BIRD, J.: Antiquity and migrations of the early inhabitants of Patagonia. *Geographical Rev.*, 28:250-275, 1938.

————: Before Magellan. *Natur. Hist.*, 41:16-28, 1938.

BIRDSELL, J. B.: Some environmental and cultural factors influencing the structuring of Australian aboriginal populations. *Am. Naturalist*, 87:171-207, 1953.

————: Some population problems involving Pleistocene man. *Cold Spring Harbor Symposia on Quantitative Biology*, 22:47-69, 1957.

BIRKET-SMITH, K.: *The Eskimos*, 2nd ed. London, Methuen, 1959.

BISSONNETTE, T. H.: Sexual photoperiodism. *Quart. Rev. Biol.*, 11:371-386, 1936.

BLACK, D.: Asia and the dispersal of the primates. *Bull. Geol. Soc. Am.*, 4: 1925.

BLUM, H. H.: *Photodynamic Action and Diseases Caused by Light.* New York, Reinhold, 1941.

BLUMENBACH, J. F.: *On the Natural Variety of Mankind* (translated by Bendyshe, T.), *The Anthropological Treatises of Johann Friedrich Blumenbach.* London, Anthropological Society, 1865.

BOAS, F.: *Changes in Bodily Form of Descendants of Immigrants.* (*Final Report.*) Washington, Government Printing Office, 1911 (61st Congress, 2nd Session, Senate Document 208), Reprinted, New York, Columbia Univ. Press, 1912.

————: *Anthropology and Modern Life*, 2nd ed. New York, Norton, 1932.

————: *The Mind of Primitive Man*, 2nd ed. New York, Macmillan, 1938.

————: Racial purity. *Asia*, 40:231-234, 1940.

————: *Race, Language, and Culture.* New York, Macmillan, 1940.

————: *Race and Democratic Society.* New York, Augustin, 1945.

BOETTGER, C. R.: *Die Haustiere Afrikas.* Jena, Fischer, 1958.

BOLK, L.: *Das Problem der Menschwerdung.* Jena, Fischer, 1926.

————: Origin of racial characteristics in man. *Amer. J. Phys. Anthropol.*, 13: 1-28, 1929.

BONIN, G. VON: On the size of man's brain, as indicated by skull capacity. *J. Comp. Neurol.*, 59:1-28, 1934.

BOULE, M. and VALLOIS, H. V.: *Fossil Man.* New York, Dryden Press, 1957.

BOULENGER, E. G.: *Apes and Monkeys.* London, Harrap, 1936.

Boyd, W. C.: Blood groups. *Tabulae Biologicae, 17:*111-240, 1939.

———: Rh blood factors; an orientation review. *Arch. Path., 40:*114-127, 1945.

———: Critique of methods of classifying mankind. *Am. J. Phys. Anthropol., 27:*333-364, 1940.

———: Gene frequencies and race mixture. *Am. J. Phys. Anthropol.,* n.s. *7:*587-593, 1949.

———: *Genetics and the Races of Man.* Boston, Little, Brown, 1950.

———: *Genetics and the Races of Man.* Boston, Boston Univ. Press, 1958.

———: Has statistics retarded the progress of physical anthropology? *Am. J. Phys. Anthropol.,* n.s. *16:*481-484, 1959.

Braidwood, R. J.: *Prehistoric Men,* 3rd Ed. Chicago, Chicago Natural History Museum, 1957, Popular Series, No. 37.

———: Near Eastern Prehistory. *Science, 127:*1419-1430, 1958.

———, and Reed, C. E.: The achievement and early consequences of food production: a consideration of the archaeological and Natural-Historical Evidence. *Cold Spring Harbor Symposia on Quantitative Biology, 22:*19-31, 1957.

Bransby, E. R. and Gelling, J. W.: Variations in and the effect of weather on the growth of children. *Medical Officer, 75:*213-217, 1946.

Brash, J. C., McKeag, H. T. A. and Scott, J. H.: *The Aetiology of Irregularity and Malocclusion of the Teeth,* 2nd Ed. London, Dental Board of the United Kingdom, 1956.

Breuil, H. and Lantier, R.: *Les Hommes De La Pierre Ancienne (Paléolithique et Mésolithique).* Paris, 1959.

Briggs, L. C.: The Stone Age Races of North Africa. American School of Prehistoric Research, Peabody Museum, Harvard University, Bulletin No. 18, Cambridge, Mass., 1955.

———: The Living Races of the Sahara Desert. *Papers of the Peabody Museum of Archaeology and Ethnology, Harvard University,* 28:xii+217, 1958.

Broom, R.: *Finding the Missing Link.* London, Watts, 1950.

———: The genera and species of the South African fossil ape-men. *Am. J. Phys. Anthropol.,* n.s. *8:*1-13, 1950.

——— and Robinson, J. T.: *Swartkrans Ape-Man: Paranthropus crassidens.* Pretoria, Transvaal Museum Memoir No. 6, 1952.

——— and Schepers, G. W. H.: *The South African Fossil Ape-Men.* Pretoria, Transvaal Museum Memoir No. 2, 1946.

——— and Robinson, J. T. and Schepers, G. W. H.: *Sterkfontein Ape-Men: Plesianthropus.* Pretoria, Transvall Museum Memoir No. 4, 1950.

Brown, F. M.: The microscopy of mammalian hair for anthropologists. *Proc. Amer. Phil. Soc., 85:*250-274, 1942.

Brues, A. M.: Identification of skeletal remains. *J. Crim. Law Criminol. & Police Science, 48:*551-563, 1958.

———: Regional differences in the physical characteristics of an American population. *Am. J. Phys. Anthropol.,* n.s. *4:*463-482, 1946.

Brzezinski, J., Gurevitch, J., Hermoni, D. and Mandel, G.: Bloodgroups in Jews from Yemen. *Ann. Eugenics, 16:*331-33, 1951.

Budtz-Olsen, O. E.: Haptoglobins and hemoglobins in Australian aborigines, with a simple method for the estimation of haptoglobins. *Med. J. Australia,* pp. 689-692, Nov. 22, 1958.

BUETTNER-JANUSCH, J.: Natural selection in man: The ABO(H) blood group system. *Am. Anthropol.*, 61:437-456, 1959.

BULLEN, A. K. (editor): Development of high civilizations in hot climates. *Florida Anthropologist*, 4:101-149, 1953.

CAIN, A. J.: Possible significance of secretor. *The Lancet*, 1:212-213, 1957.

CALHOUN, J. B.: The social aspects of population dynamics. *J. Mammal.*, 33:139-159, 1952.

CALMAN, W. T.: *The Classification of Animals.* New York, Wiley, 1949.

CANDELA, P. B.: The introduction of blood-group B into Europe. *Human Biol.*, 14:413-443, 1942.

———— and Goss, L. J.: Blood-group factors in the blood organs, and secretions of primates. *J. Immunol.*, 45:229-235, 1942.

CARPENTER, C. R.: A field study of the behavior and social relations of howling monkeys. *Compt. Psychol. Monogr.*, 10:1-167, 1934, Serial no. 48.

————: A field study in Siam of the behavior and social relations of the gibbon (*Hylobates lar*). *Compt. Psychol. Monogr.*, 16:1-212, 1940, Serial no. 84.

CARTER, G. F.: *Pleistocene Man at San Diego.* Baltimore, Johns Hopkins Press, 1957.

CASSIRER, E.: *An Essay on Man.* New Haven, Yale University Press, 1944.

CASSON, S.: *The Discovery of Man.* New York, Harper, 1940.

CASTLE, W. E.: Biological and social consequences of race crossing. *Am. J. Phys. Anthropol.*, 9:145-156, 1926.

————: Race mixture and physical disharmonies. *Science*, 71:603-606, 1930.

CATTELL, R. B. and MOLTENO, V.: Contributions concerning mental inheritance. II. Temperament. *J. Genet. Psychol.*, 57:31-42, 1940.

CAVE, A. J. E.: Report on a human calvaria of upper paleolithic type. *Archaeologia*, 92:117-119, 1947.

CAWLEY, R. H., MCKEOWN, T. and RECORD, R. G.: Influence of pre-natal environment on post-natal growth. *Br. J. Prev. Soc. Med.*, 8:66-69, 1954.

CAZIER, M. A. and BACON, A. L.: Introduction to quantitative systematics. *Bull. Amer. Mus. Nat. Hist.*, 93:347-388, 1949.

CEPPELINI, R.: The usefulness of blood factors in racial anthropology. *Am. J. Phys. Anthropol.*, 13:389, 1955.

CHALMERS, J. N. M., IKIN, E. W. and A. E. MOURANT: The ABO, MN and Rh blood groups of the Basque people. *Am. J. Phys. Anthropol.*, n.s., 7:529-544, 1949.

———— and LAWLER, S. D.: Data on linkage in man: elliptocytosis and blood groups. II. Families 1 and 2, *Ann. Eugenics*, 17:267-271, 1953.

CHAMBERS, E. G.: *Statistical Calculation for Beginners.* New York: Cambridge University Press, 1948.

CHARD, C. S.: New World migration routes. Anthrop. Papers Univ. Alaska, 1:23-26, 1959.

CHILDE, V. G.: *Man Makes Himself.* New York, New American Library, 1946.

————: *What Happened in History.* New York, New American Library, 1946.

————: *The Dawn of European Civilization,* 6th ed. New York, Knopf, 1958.

————: *A Short Introduction to Archaeology.* London, Muller, 1956.

CHOWN, B.: Problems in blood group analysis. *Am. Anthropol.*, 59:885-888, 1957.

CHU, E. H. Y. and GILES, N. H.: A study of primate chromosome complements. *Amer. Nat.*, 91:273-282, 1957.

————: Human chromosome complements in normal somatic cells in culture. *Am. J. Hum. Genetics, 11:*63-79, 1958.

CLARK, J. D.: *The Prehistory of Southern Africa.* New York, Harper, 1959.

————, OAKLEY, K. P., WELLS, L. H. and McCLELLAND: New studies on Rhodesian man. *J. Roy. Anthropol. Inst., 77:*7-32, 1947.

CLARK, J. G. D.: *Prehistoric Europe.* London, Methuen, New York, Philosophical Library, 1952.

————: *Excavations at Starr Carr.* Cambridge: at the University Press, New York, Cambridge Univ. Press, 1954.

————: *Archaeology and Society.* Cambridge, Mass., Harvard Univ. Press, 1957.

CLARK, W. E. LE GROS: *Early Forerunners of Man.* Baltimore, Wood, 1934.

————: Pithecanthropus in Peking. *Antiquity, 19:*1-5, 1945.

————: *History of Primates,* 6th ed. London, British Museum (Natural History), 1958.

————: New palaeontological evidence bearing on the evolution of the Hominoidea. *Quart. J. Geol. Soc.,* (London), *105:*225-264, 1949.

————: *The Fossil Evidence for Human Evolution.* Chicago, Univ. Chicago Press, 1955.

————: Bones of contention. *J. Roy. Anthropol. Inst., 88:*1-15, 1958.

————: *The Antecedents of Man.* Edinburgh, University of Edinburgh Press, 1959.

CLARKE, C. A., *et al.*: ABO groups and secretor character in duodenal ulcer. Population and sibship studies. *Brit. Med. J., 2:*725-731, 1956.

CLARKE, C. A., *et al.*: Secretion of blood group antigens and peptic ulcer. *Brit. Med. J., 1:*603-607, 1959.

COBB, W. M.: The physical constitution of the American Negro. *J. Negro Education, 3:*340-388, 1934.

COLBERT, E. A.: Some paleontological principles significant in human evolution. In *Early Man in the Far East* (edited by W. W. Howells), p. 103-147.

————: *Evolution of the Vertebrates.* New York, Wiley, 1955.

COLE, S.: *The Prehistory of East Africa.* Baltimore, Penguin Books, 1954.

COLIN, E. C.: *Elements of Genetics,* 3rd ed. New York, McGraw-Hill, 1956.

COLLIER, K. G.: *The Science of Humanity.* New York, Nelson, 1950.

COMAS, J.: *Manual of Physical Anthropology.* Springfield, Ill., C C Thomas, 1960.

CONKLIN, E. G.: *Heredity and Environment.* Princeton Univ. Press, 1939.

————: *Man: Real and Ideal.* New York, Scribner's, 1943.

COOKE, H. B. S., MALAN, B. D., and WELLS, L. H.: Fossil man in the Lebombo Mountains, South Africa: The 'Border Cave.' *Man, 45:*6-13, 1945.

COON, C. S.: *The Races of Europe.* New York, Macmillan, 1939.

————: *The Story of Man.* New York, Knopf, 1954.

————: Some problems of human variability and natural selection in climate and culture. *Amer. Nat., 89:*257-280, 1955.

————: *The Seven Caves.* New York, Knopf, 1957.

————: Climate and race. In Harlow Shapley (editor): *Climatic Change.* Harvard Univ. Press, 1954, 13-34.

————, GARN, S. M., and BIRDSELL, J. B.: *Races.* Springfield, Thomas, 1950.

CORNER, G. W.: *Ourselves Unborn.* New Haven, Yale Univ. Press, 1944.

CORNWALL, I. W.: *Bones for the Archaeologist.* New York, Macmillan, 1956.

————: *Soils for the Archaeologist.* New York, Macmillan, 1958.

COWLES, R. B.: The black skin and human protective coloration. *J. Entomol. &
Zoology,* 42:1-4, 1950.

CRAVEN, B. and JOKL, E.: A note on the effect of training on the physique of
adolescent boys. *Clin. Proc. J. Cape Town Post-Graduate Med. A.,* 5:18-19,
1946.

CRICK, F. H. C.: Nucleic acids. *Scientific Amer., 197:*188-200, 1958.

CUDMORE, S. A. and NEAL, N. A.: *A Height and Weight Survey of Toronto Elementary School Children 1939.* Ottawa, Ministry of Trade and Commerce,
1942.

CUENOT, L.: L'homme ce néoténique. *Bull. L'Acad. Roy. Belg.,* 31: 1945.

————: *L'Evolution Biologique.* Paris, Masson, 1951.

CUMMINS, H. and MIDLO, C.: *Finger Prints, Palms and Soles: An Introduction
to Dermatoglyphics.* Philadelphia, Blakiston, 1943.

DAHLBERG, G.: An analysis of the conception of race and a new method of dis-
tinguishing races. *Human Biol.,* 14:372-385, 1942.

————: *Race, Reason and Rubbish: a Primer of Race Biology.* New York, Columbia Univ. Press, 1942.

————: Environment, inheritance and random variations with special reference
to investigations on twins. *Acta Genet. et Statistica Medica, Basle, 1: 1;* 104-
114, 1948.

————: *Statistical Methods for Medical and Biological Students.* New York,
Norton, 1948.

DANSEREAU, P.: *A Universal System for Recording Vegetation.* Institut Botanique
de L'Université de Montréal, Montreal, 1958.

DARLINGTON, C. D. and HAQUE, A.: Chromosomes of monkeys and men, *Nature,
175:*32, 1955.

————: The origin of Darwinism. *Scientific Amer., 200:*60-66, 1959.

DART, R. A.: Taungs and its significance. *Natural History,* 26:315-327, 1926.

————: The Makapansgat proto-human Australopithecus prometheus. *Am. J.
Phys. Anthropol.,* n.s. 6:391-411, 1948.

————: The predatory implemental technique of Australopithecus. *Am. J. Phys.
Anthropol.,* n.s. 7:1-38, 1949.

————: Innominate fragments of Australopithecus prometheus. *Am. J. Phys.
Anthropol.,* n.s. 7:301-333, 1949.

————: A second adult palate of Australopithecus prometheus. *Am. J. Phys.
Anthropol.,* n.s. 7:335-338, 1949.

————: The cranio-facial fragment of Australopithecus prometheus. *Am. J. Phys.
Anthropol.,* n.s. 7:187-214, 1949.

————: The second, or adult, female mandible of Australopithecus prometheus.
Am. J. Phys. Anthropol., n.s. 12:313-344, 1954.

————: The first Australopithecine fragment from the Makapansgat pebble culture stratum. *Nature,* 176:170, 1955.

————: The minimal bone-breccia content of Makapansgat and the australopithecine habit. *Am. Anthropol.,* 60:923-931, 1958.

————: An 'Australopithecine' scoop from Herefordshire. *Nature, 183:*844, 1959.

————: A further adolescent australopithecine ilium from Makapansgat. *Am. J.
Phys. Anthropol.,* n.s., 16:473-479, 1959.

———— and CRAIG, D.: *Adventures with the Missing Link.* New York, Harper,
1959.

164 A HANDBOOK OF ANTHROPOMETRY

DAS, S. R.: A contribution to the heredity of the P.T.C. taste character based on a study of 845 sib pairs. *Ann. Hum. Genetics, 20*:334-343, 1956.
DARWIN, C.: *The Descent of Man.* London, Murray, 1871.
———: *The Origin of Species.* London, Murray, 1859.
DAVENPORT, C.: Heredity of hair form in man. *Am. Naturalist, 42*:341, 1908.
———: *The Heredity of Skin Color in Negro-White Crosses.* Washington, Carnegie Inst., 1913, publication 188.
———: *Guide to Physical Anthropometry and Anthroposcopy.* Cold Spring Harbor, New York, Eugenics Research Association, 1927.
——— and STEGGERDA, M.: *Race Crossing in Jamaica.* Washington, Carnegie Inst., 1929.
DAVIS, A.: The distribution of the blood-groups and its bearing on the concept of race. In *Political Arithmetic* (edited by Hogben, L.), New York, Macmillan, 1941.
DAY, C. B.: *A Study of Some Negro-White Families in the United States.* Cambridge, Peabody Museum, Harvard University, 1932.
DE BEER, G.: *Embryos and Ancestors.* New York, Oxford Univ. Press, 1958.
DE CHARDIN, T.: *The Phenomenon of Man.* New York, Harper, 1959.
DE LAET, S. J.: *Archaeology and its Problems.* New York, Macmillan, 1957.
DE RODRÍGUEZ, M. L. G., and ARENDS, T.: Distribution of haptoglobins in native Venezuelans. *Nature, 183*:1465-1466, 1959.
DE TERRA, H.: Geology and climate as factors of human evolution in Asia. In *Early Man in the Far East* (edited by W. W. Howells), p. 7-15, Philadelphia, The Wistar Institute, 1949.
———: New approach to the problem of man's origin. *Science, 124*:1282-1285, 1956.
———, ROMERO, J. and STEWART, T. D.: *Tepexpan Man. Viking Fund Publications in Anthropology,* No. 11. New York, Viking Fund, 1949.
DE VRIES, H., and OAKLEY, K. P.: Radiocarbon dating of the Piltdown skull and jaw. *Nature, 184*:224-226, 1959.
DHYRENFURTH, N. G.: Film making for scientific field workers. *Amer. Anthropol., 54*:147-152, 1952.
DICE, L. R.: *Man's Nature and Nature's Man.* Ann Arbor, Univ. Michigan Press, 1955.
DINGWALL, E. J.: *Artificial Cranial Deformation.* London, John Bale, 1931.
DOBZHANSKY, TH.: *Genetics and the Origin of Species,* 3rd edition. New York, Columbia Univ. Press, 1951.
———: On species and races of living and fossil man. *Am. J. Phys. Anthropol.,* n.s. 2. 251-265, 1944.
———: Genetics and human affairs. *The Teaching Biologist, 12*:97-106, 1943.
———: The genetic basis of evolution. *Scientific American, 182*:32-41.
———: Human diversity and adaptation. In *Cold Spring Harbor Symposia on Quantitative Biology.* Long Island, New York, 1950, pp. 385-400.
———: *Evolution, Genetics, and Man.* New York, Wiley, 1957.
———: *The Biological Basis of Human Freedom.* New York, Columbia Univ. Press, 1956.
——— and HOLZ, A. M.: A re-examination of the problem of manifold effects of genes in *Drosophila melanogaster. Genetics, 28*:301, 1943.

———— and Montagu, M. F. Ashley: Natural selection and the mental capacities of mankind. *Science, 105:*587-590, 1947.

———— and Wallace, B.: The problem of adaptive differences in human populations. *Amer. J. Hum. Genetics, 6:*199-206, 1954.

Dornfeldt, W.: Studien uber Schädelform und Schädelveränderung von Berliner Ostjuden und ihren Kindern. *Ztschr. Morphol. u. Anthropol., 39:*290-372, 1941.

Draper, G., Dupertuis, C. W. and Caughey, J. L., Jr.: *Human Constitution and Clinical Medicine.* New York, Hoeber, 1944.

Drennan, M. R.: A note on the morphological status of the Swanscombe and Fontéchevade skulls. *Am. J. Phys. Anthropol.,* n.s. *14:*73-83, 1956.

————: The special features and status of the Saldanha skull. *Am. J. Anthropol.,* n.s. *13:*625-634, 1955.

————: Pedomorphism in the pre-Bushman skull. *Am. J. Phys. Anthropol., 16:*203-210, 1931.

————: The role of sex in human evolution. *S. Afr. Med. J., 32:*1175-1178, 1958.

———— and Singer, R.: A mandibular fragment probably of the Saldanha skull. *Nature, 1:* 1955.

DuBrul, E. L.: *Evolution of the Speech Apparatus.* Springfield, Thomas, 1958.

Dunn, L. C.: *Heredity and Evolution in Human Populations.* Cambridge, Harvard Univ. Press. 1959.

———— and Dobzhansky, Th.: *Heredity, Race and Society.* New York, New American Library, 1952.

Dunsford, I. and Bowley, C. C.: *Techniques in Blood-Grouping.* Springfield, Thomas, 1956.

Dupertuis, C. W. and Tanner, J. M.: The pose of the subject for photogrammetric anthropometry, with especial reference to somatotyping. *Am. J. Phys. Anthropol.,* n.s. *8:*27-44, 1950.

East, E. M. and Jones, D. F.: *Inbreeding and Outbreeding.* Philadelphia, Lippincott, 1919.

Edwards, E. A. and Duntley, S. Q.: The pigments and color of living skin. *Am. J. Anatomy, 45:*1-33, 1939.

Ehrich, R. W. and Coon, C. S.: Occipital flattening among the Dinarics. *Am. J. Phys. Anthropol.,* n.s., *6:*181-186, 1947.

Elderton, E. M.: Height and weight of school children in Glasgow. *Biometrika, 10:*288-340, 1914.

Elliot, D. G.: *A Review of the Primates,* 3 vols., New York, Am. Museum of Natur. Hist., 1913.

Emiliani, C.: Note on absolute chronology of human evolution. *Science, 123:* 924-926, 1956.

Engelmann, G. J.: Age of first menstruation on the North American continent. *Tr. Am. Gynec. Soc., 26:*77-101, 1901.

Etcheverry, M. A.: El factor rhesus, su genetica e importancia clinica. *Dia Med., 17:*1237-1251, 1945.

————: El factor rhesus en Personas de Ascendencia Iberica residentes en la Argentina. *Semana Méd.,* Nov. *25:*500, 1947.

Evans, F. G.: The names of fossil men. *Science, 102:*16-17, 1945.

Evans, R. D.: Quantitative inferences concerning the genetic effects of radiation on human beings. *Science, 109:*299-304, 1949.

Evernden, J. F., Curtis, G. H., and Kistler, R.: Potassium-argon dating of pleistocene volcanoes. *Quaternaria, 4:*13-17, 1957.

FALCONER, D. S.: Sensory threshold for solutions of Phenyl-Thio-Carbamide. *Ann. Eugen., 13*:211-222, 1947.

FINKELSTEIN, L. (editor): *The Jews*, 2 vols. New York, Harper, 1950.

FISCHER, E.: *Die Rehobother Bastards und das Bastardierungs-problem beim Menschen.* Jena, 1913.

FISHBERG, M.: *The Jews.* New York, Scribners, 1911.

FISHER, R. A.: *The Genetical Theory of Natural Selection.* Oxford, Clarendon Press, 1930.

———: *Statistical Methods for Research Workers*, 10th edition. Edinburgh, Oliver & Boyd, 1948.

——— and TAYLOR, G. L.: Scandinavian influence in Scottish Ethnology. *Nature, 145*:590, 1940.

———, FORD, E. B. and HUXLEY, J. S.: Taste-testing the anthropoid apes. *Nature, 144*:750, 1939.

FITT, A. B.: *Seasonal Influence on Growth, Function and Inheritance.* London, Oxford, 1941.

———: The heights and weights of men according to month of birth. *Human Biology, 27*:138-142, 1955.

FLYNN, F. V. and DeMAYO, P.: Micro-electrophoresis of protein on filter paper. *The Lancet, 2*:235, 1951.

FORBES, H. O.: *Monkeys*, 2 vols. London, Shaw, 1894.

FOX, A. L.: The relationship between chemical constitution and taste. *Proc. Nat. Acad. Sc., 18*:115-120, 1932.

FRANZBLAU, A. N.: *A Primer of Statistics for Non-Statisticians.* New York, Harcourt, Brace, 1958.

FYLEMAN, R.: *Monkeys.* New York, Nelson, 1936.

GALATIUS-JENSEN, F.: Further investigations of the genetic mechanism of the haptoglobins. *Acta Genet., 7*:549, 1957.

———: On the genetics of the haptoglobins. *Acta Genetica et Statistica Medica, 8*:232-247, 1958.

GALLOWAY, A.: Man in Africa in the light of recent discoveries. *South African J. Sc., 34*:89-120, 1937.

———: Physical Anthropology in South and East Africa. *Yearbook of Physical Anthropology, 4*:40-46, 1949.

GALTON, D. A. G. (editor): *Haematology.* Brit. Med. Bull., *15*:1-88, 1959.

GALTON, F.: *Inquiries Into the Human Faculty and its Development.* London, Macmillan, 1883.

GARN, S. M.: Types and replacement of hair volume. *Ann. N. Y. Acad. Sc., 53*: 498-527, 1951.

———: The measurement of skin temperature. *Am. J. Phys. Anthropol.*, n.s. *12*:1-4, 1954.

——— and COON, C. S.: On the number of races of mankind. *Amer. Anthropol., 57*:996-1001, 1955.

——— and LEWIS, A. B.: Tooth size, and "giant" fossil man. *Amer. Anthropol., 60*:874-880, 1958.

——— and SHAMIR, Z.: *Methods For Research in Human Growth.* Springfield, Thomas, 1958.

GATES, R. R.: *Human Genetics*, 2 vols. New York, Macmillan, 1946.

———: The African Pygmies. *Acta Gen. Med. et Gemell., 8*:159-218, 1958.

GAVAN, J. A., WASHBURN, S. L. and LEWIS, P. H.: Photography: an anthropometric tool. *Am. J. Phys. Anthropol.*, n.s., *10*:331-353, 1952.

GAZIN, C. L.: A review of the middle and upper Eocene primates of North America. *Smithsonian Miscellaneous Collections, 136*:1-112, 1958.

GENET-VARCIN, E.: *Les Négritos de l'Isle de Luçon* (*Philippines*). Paris, Masson et Cie., 1951.

GENOVÉS, S.: The problem of the sex of certain fossil hominids, with special reference to the Neanderthal skeletons from Spy. *J. Roy. Anthropol. Inst., 84:* 131-144, 1954.

GEOGEGAN, B.: The determination of body measurement, surface area and body volume by photography. *Am. J. Phys. Anthrop.*, n.s., *11*:97-119, 1943.

GERASIMOV, M. M.: Vosstanovlenie litsa po cherepu. *Izdatel'stvo Akademii Nauk SSSR*, Moscow, 1955. (Reconstruction of the features on the skull).

GIBLETT, E. R.: Haptoglobin types in American Negroes. *Nature, 183*:192-193, 1959.

———: Js, a new blood group antigen found in Negroes. *Nature, 181*:1221-1222, 1958.

——— and CHASE, J.: Js^a, a "new" red-cell antigen found in Negroes; evidence for an eleventh blood group system. *Brit. J. Haemat., 5*:319-326, 1959.

GILL, E. D.: Radiocarbon dates for Australian archaeological and geological samples. *Austral. J. Sc., 18*:49, 1955.

GILLIN, J. (editor): *For A Science of Social Man.* New York, Macmillan, 1954.

GLASS, B.: On the evidence of random genetic drift in human populations. *Amer. J. Phys. Anthropol.*, n.s., *14*:541-555.

———: Genetic changes in human populations, especially those due to gene flow and genetic drift. *Advances in Genetics, 6*:95-139, 1954.

———, SACKS, M. S., JAHN, E. F. and HESS, C.: Genetic drift in a religious isolate: an analysis of the causes of variation in blood group and other gene frequencies in a small population. *Amer. Nat., 86*:145-160, 1952.

GODLEY, E. J.: Blood group frequencies in New Zealand and Maori soldiers. *Ann. Eugenics, 13*:211-222, 1947.

GODYCKI, M.: Sur la certitude de détermination du sexe d'après le fémur, le cubitus, et l'humérus. *Bull. et Mém. de la Soc. d'Anthrop. Paris, 8*:405-410, 1957.

GOLDSMITH, K. L. G. (editor): Blood Groups. *Brit. Med. Bull., 15*:89-174, 1959.

GOLDSTEIN, M. S.: *Demographic and Bodily Changes in Descendants of Mexican Immigrants.* Austin, Texas, Inst. Latin-American Stud., 1943.

———: Theory of survival of the unfit. *J. Nat. Med. A., 47*:223-226, 1955.

GRAUBARD, M.: *Man, the Slave and Master.* New York, Covici-Friede, 1938.

GRAY, M. P.: A method for reducing non-specific reactions in the typing of human skeletal material. *Am. J. Phys. Anthropol.*, n.s., *16*:135-139, 1958.

GREENBERG, J. H.: Current trends in linguistics. *Science, 130*:1165-1174, 1959.

GREGORY, W. K.: Studies on the evolution of the primates. *Bull. Am. Museum Natur. Hist., 35*:239-255, 1916.

———: *The Origin and Evolution of the Human Dentition.* Baltimore, Williams & Wilkins, 1922.

———: *Our Face From Fish to Man.* New York, Putnam, 1929.

———: *Man's Place Among the Anthropoids.* New York, Oxford Univ. Press, 1934.

———: The bearing of the Australopithecinae upon the problem of man's place in nature. *Am. J. Phys. Anthropol.*, n.s. *7*:485-512, 1949.

────── and HELLMAN, M.: The dentition of Dryopithecus and the origin of man. *Anthrop. Papers, Amer. Mus. Nat. Hist.*, 28:1-123, 1926.

──────: The dentition of the extinct South African Man-Ape *Australopithecus* (*Plesianthropus*) *transvaalensis* Broom. A comparative and phylogenetic study. *Ann. Transvaal Mus.*, 19:359-373, 1939.

GREULICH, W. W.: Growth of children of the same race under different environmental conditions. *Science, 127*:515-516, 1958.

──────: A comparison of the physical growth and development of American-born and native Japanese children. *Am. J. Phys. Anthropol., n.s. 15*:489-515, 1957.

────── and PYLE, S. I.: *Radiographic Atlas of Skeletal Development of the Hand and Wrist.* Stanford, Stanford Univ. Press, 1959.

Growth and Development of the Child. Part II. Anatomy and Physiology. New York, Century Co., 1933.

GRIMM, H.: Altern, lebensdauer, krankheit und tod bei vorgesdrichtlichen und frühgeschichtlichen bevölkerungsgruppen. *Wissensch. Ann.*, 3:171-180, 1956.

GROSS, H.: Mastodon, mammoth and man in America. *Bull. Texas Archeol. & Paleontol. Soc.*, 22:101-131, 1951.

GRÜNEBERG, H.: *Animal Genetics and Medicine.* London, Hamish Hamilton, 1947.

GUREVITCH, J., HERMONI, D. and POLISHUK, Z.: Rh blood types in Jerusalem "Jews." *Ann. Eugenics, 16*:129-130, 1951.

GUTHE, G. E.: Notes on the cephalic index of Russian Jews in Boston. *Am. J. Phys. Anthropol.*, 1:213-223, 1918.

HADDON, A. C.: *The Wanderings of Peoples.* New York, Macmillan, 1911.

──────: *History of Anthropology.* London, Watts, 1934.

──────: *The Races of Man.* New York, Cambridge Univ. Press, 1924.

HALDANE, J. B. S.: *The Causes of Evolution.* New York, Longmans, 1935.

──────: *Heredity and Politics.* New York, Norton, 1938.

──────: The blood-group frequencies of European peoples, and racial origins. *Human Biol., 12*:457-480, 1940.

──────: *New Paths in Genetics.* New York, Harper, 1942.

──────: Disease and evolution. Symposium sui Fattori Ecologici e Genetici della Speciazioni negli Animali. *La Ricerca Scientifica, 19*:1-11, 1949.

──────: The argument from animals to men. *J. Roy. Anthropol. Inst., 86*:1-14, 1956.

HALLIDAY, J. L.: *Psychosocial Medicine.* New York, W. W. Norton, 1948.

HALLOWELL, A. I.: Personality structure and evolution. *Amer. Anthropol., 52*: 159-173, 1950.

──────: The structural and functional dimensions of a human existence. *Quart. Rev. Biol., 31*:88-101, 1957.

HAMBLY, W. D.: Cranial capacity, a study in methods. *Fieldiana Anthropol.* (Chicago Natural History Museum), 36:25-75, 1947.

HAMMOND, W. H.: The status of physical types. *Hum. Biol., 29*:223-241, 1957.

HANKINS, F. H.: *The Racial Basis of Civilization.* New York, Knopf, 1931.

HARRINGTON, M. R.: Man's oldest date in America. *Natural History, 64*:512-517, 1955.

HARRIS, D. B. (editor): *The Concept of Development.* Minneapolis, Univ. Minnesota Press, 1957.

HARRIS, H.: *Human Biochemical Genetics.* London and New York, Cambridge University Press, 1959.

——— and KALMUS, H.: The measurement of taste sensitivity to phenylthiouria (P.T.C.). *Ann. Eugenics,* 15:24-31, 1949.

HARRISON, R. J.: *Man the Peculiar Animal.* Baltimore, Penguin Books, 1958.

HECHST, B.: Über einen Fall von Mikroencephalie ohne Geistigen Defekt. *Arch. f. Psych. u. Nervenkr.,* 97:64-76, 1932.

HEIZER, R. F. (editor): *The Archaeologist at Work.* New York, Harper, 1959.

HERSKOVITS, M. J.: *The American Negro.* New York, Knopf, 1928.

HERTZBERG, H. T. E., DUPERTUIS, C. W. and EMANUEL, I.: Stereophotogrammetry as an anthropometric tool. *Photogrammetric Engineering,* 23:942-947, 1957.

HERTZBERG, H. T. E. (editor): Annotated bibliography of applied physical anthropology in human engineering. Aero Medical Laboratory, Wright-Patterson Air Force Base, Ohio, 1958.

HIBBEN, F. C.: *Prehistoric Man in Europe.* Norman, Oklahoma, Univ. Oklahoma Press, 1958.

———: Specimens from Sandia Cave and their possible significance. *Science,* 122:688-689, 1955.

HIERNAUX, J.: Physical anthropology and the frequency of genes with a selective value: the sickle cell gene. *Am. J. Phys. Anthropol.,* n.s. 13:455-472, 1955.

HILL, A. B.: *Principles of Medical Statistics,* 6th ed. New York, Oxford Univ. Press, 1955.

HILL, W. C. OSMAN: *Man's Ancestry.* Springfield, Thomas, 1954.

———: *Primates: Comparative Anatomy and Taxonomy.* I. *Strepsirhini.* II. *Haplorhini.* III. *Pithecoidea.* New York, Interscience Publishers, 1953, 1955, 1957.

HOFER, H., SCHULTZ, A. H. and STARK, D. (editors): *Primatologia,* 3 vols. Basel, S. Karger A. G., 1956, 1959.

HOGBEN, L.: The concept of race. In *Genetic Principles in Medicine and Social Science.* New York, Knopf, 1932, p. 122-144.

———: *Genetic Principles in Medicine and Social Science.* New York, Knopf, 1932.

——— (editor): *Political Arithmetic.* New York, Macmillan, 1938.

HONIGMANN, J. J.: *Culture and Personality.* New York, 1954.

HOOTON, E. A.: The making and mixing of human races. In *Twilight of Man.* New York, Putnam, 1939, p. 60-192.

———: *Crime and the Man.* Cambridge, Harvard Univ. Press, 1939.

———: *The American Criminal.* Cambridge, Harvard Univ. Press, 1939.

———: *Man's Poor Relations.* New York, Doubleday, Doran, 1942.

———: *Up From the Ape,* 2nd edition. New York, Macmillan, 1946.

HOPWOOD, A. T.: Miocene primates from Kenya. *J. Linnaean Soc. London,* (Zoology), 37:437-464, 1933.

HOWARD, E. G.: Evidence of early man in North America. *The Museum Journal* (University of Pennsylvania), 24:53-171, 1935.

HOWELL, E. C.: The place of Neanderthal man in human evolution. *Amer. J. Phys. Anthropol.,* n.s. 9:379-416.

———: Pleistocene glacial ecology and the evolution of "classic Neanderthal" man. *Southwest. J. Anthropol.,* 8:377-410, 1952.

———: The evolutionary significance of variation and varieties of "Neanderthal" man. *Quart. Rev. Biol.,* 32:330-347, 1957.

————: Upper Pleistocene men of the southwest Asian Mousterian. *Trans. Int. Neanderthal Cent. Congress*, Utrecht, Kemink en Zn, 1958, pp. 185-198.

————: Upper Pleistocene stratigraphy and early man in the Levant. *Proc. Amer. Phil. Soc.*, *103*:1-65, 1959.

HOWELLS, W. W.: *Mankind in The Making*, 2nd ed. New York, Doubleday, 1959.

———— (editor): Early Man in the Far East. *Studies in Physical Anthropology*, No. 1, Philadelphia, Wistar Inst., 1949.

————: *Variation of External Body Form in the Individual*. Peabody Museum Cambridge, Mass., 1957.

————: *Back of History*. New York, Doubleday, 1954.

HOYLE, L. E.: Physical anthropology and its instruments: an historical study. *Southwest. J. Anthropol.*, *9*:408-430, 1953.

HRDLIČKA, A.: *Early Man in South America*. Smithsonian Institution, Bureau of Ethnology, Bulletin, 52, 1912.

————: *The Skeletal Remains of Early Man*. Washington, Smithsonian Miscellaneous Collections, vol. 83, 1930.

————: *The Old Americans*. Baltimore, Williams and Wilkins, 1925.

————: *Practical Anthropometry* 3rd edition (edited by Stewart, T. D.), Philadelphia, Wistar Inst., 1947.

HUE, E.: *Crânes paleolithiques. Bibliographie*. In Congrès Prehistorique de France, XIIᵉ Session, Toulouse-Foix, 1936, pp. 113-285. Paris, Société Prehistorique Française, 1937.

HUNT, JR., E. E.: Anthropometry, genetics, and racial history. *Am. Anthropol.*, *61*:64-87, 1959.

HUNTINGTON, E.: *Mainsprings of Civilization*. New York, Wiley, 1945.

HÜRZELER, J.: Zur systematischen Stellung von Oreopithecus. *Verh. Naturf. Ges. Basel*, *65*:88-95, 1954.

————: Oreopithecus, un point de repere pour l'histoire de l'humanite a l'ere tertaire. *Colloque Internat.* No. 60, Centre National de la Recherche Scientifique, Paris, 1956, 115-121.

————: Oreopithecus bambolii Gervais. *Ver. Naturf. Ges. Basel*, *69*:1-48, 1958.

HUXLEY, J. S.: *Evolution; the Modern Synthesis*. New York, Harper, 1942.

————: *Man Stands Alone*. New York, Harper, 1941.

————: *Evolution in Action*. New York, Harper, 1953.

————: *New Bottles For New Wine*. New York, Harper, 1957.

———— and HADDON, A. C.: *We Europeans*. New York, Harper, 1936.

HUXLEY, T. H. and HUXLEY, J.: *Touchstone For Ethics*. New York, Harper, 1947.

————: *Evidence as to Man's Place in Nature*. London, William & Norgate, 1863.

INGRAM, V. M.: How do genes act? *Scientific Amer.*, *198*:68-74, 1958.

————: Separation of the peptide chains of human globin. *Nature*, *183*:1795-1798, 1959.

ITO, P. K.: Anthropometric study of new-born infants of Japanese parents in America. *Am. J. Dis. Child.*, *52*:321-330, 1936.

————: Comparative biometrical study of physique of Japanese women born and reared under different environments. *Human Biol.*, *14*:279-351, 1942.

JACOBS, M. and STERN, B. J.: *Outline of Anthropology*. New York, Barnes & Noble, 1947.

JENNESS, D. (editor): *The American Aborigines, Their Origin and Antiquity*. Toronto, Univ. Toronto Press, 1933.

JENNINGS, H. S.: *The Biological Basis of Human Nature.* New York, Norton, 1930.

———: *Genetics.* New York, Norton, 1935.

JEPSON, G. L., MAYR, E. and SIMPSON, G. G. (editors): *Genetics, Paleontology, and Evolution,* Princeton Univ. Press, 1949.

JERISON, H. J.: Brain to body ratios and the evolution of intelligence. *Science,* 121:447-449, 1955.

JOHNSON, L. H.: Men and elephants in America. *Scientific Monthly,* 75:215-221, 1952.

JONES, F. WOODS *Man's Place Among the Mammals.* New York, Longman's, 1929.

JONSON, B.: The main frequencies of blood group genes in Sweden with special regard to the Rh genes. *Acta Gen. Med. et Gemell.,* 8:135-146, 1959.

JONXIS, J. H. P., and DELAFRESNAYE, T. F. (editors): *Abnormal Haemoglobins.* Springfield, Thomas, 1959.

JONXIS, J. H. P., and HUISMAN, T. H. J.: *A Laboratory Manual on Abnormal Haemoglobins.* Springfield, Thomas, 1959.

KABAT, E. A.: *Blood Group Substances.* New York, Academic Press, 1956.

KALLMANN, F. J.: *Heredity in Health and Mental Disorder.* New York, Norton, 1953.

——— and ANASTASIO, M. M.: Twin studies in the psychopathology of suicide. *J. Heredity,* 37:179, 1946.

KALMUS, H.: Defective colour vision, p.t.c. tasting and drepanocytosis in samples from fifteen Brazilian populations. *Ann. Hum. Genetics,* 21:313-317, 1957.

———: *Variation and Heredity.* London, Routledge, 1958.

KAPLAN, B. A.: Environment and human plasticity. *Am. Anthropol.,* 56:780-800, 1954.

KEANE, A. H.: *Man: Past and Present.* Cambridge: at the University Press, 1920.

KEEN, J. A.: A study of the differences between male and female skulls. *Am. J. Phys. Anthropol., n.s.* 8:65-79, 1950.

KEITH, A.: *The Antiquity of Man,* 2 vols. London, Williams & Norgate, 1925.

———: *Further Discoveries Relating to the Antiquity of Man.* London, Williams & Norgate, 1931.

———: *A New Theory of Human Evolution.* New York, Philosophical Library, 1949.

———: *Essays on Human Evolution.* London, Watts, 1946.

———: Foetalization as a factor in human evolution. In Keith's *A New Theory of Human Evolution.* London, Watts, 1949, pp. 192-201.

———: *An Autobiography.* London, Watts, 1950.

———: *Human Embryology and Morphology,* 6th ed. London, Arnold, 1948.

KENNEY, R. A.: Anatomical differences due to race or climate. In UNESCO Publication, Arid Zone Research VIII, *Human and Animal Ecology.* New York, Columbia Univ. Press, 1957, 83-84.

KITCHIN, F. D., *et al.:* P.T.C. taste response and thyroid disease. *Brit. Med. J.,* 1: 1069-1074, 1959.

KLINEBERG, O.: *Race Differences.* New York, Harper, 1935.

——— (editor): *Characteristics of the American Negro.* New York, Harper, 1944.

KLUCKHOHN, C.: *Mirror for Man.* New York, Whittlesey House, 1949.

——— and KELLY, W. H.: The conception of culture. In (R. Linton, editor) *The Science of Man in the World Crisis.* New York, Columbia Univ. Press, 1945.

KLUVER, H.: *Behavior Mechanisms in Monkeys.* Univ. Chicago Press, 1955.

KOENIGSWALD, G. H. R. VON: *The South African Man-Apes and Pithecanthropus.* Washington, Carnegie Inst., Publication 530, 1942, p. 205-222.

———: The discovery of early man in Java and South China. In *Early Man in the East* (edited by W. W. Howells), Philadelphia, The Wistar Institute, 1949.

———: *Gigantopithecus blacki* von Koenigswald, A giant fossil hominoid from the pleistocene of Southern China. *Anthropol. Papers. Am. Mus. Nat. Hist., 43:* 295-325, 1952.

———: *Meeting Prehistoric Man.* London, Thames & Hudson, 1956.

———: Meganthropus and the Australopithecinae. In *Third Pan-African Congress on Prehistory* (editors J. D. Clark and S. Cole). London, Chatto & Windus, 1957, pp. 158-160.

——— and WEIDENREICH, F.: The relationship between Pithecanthropus and Sinanthropus. *Nature, 144:*926-927, 1939.

KORN, N. and SMITH, H. R. (editors): *Human Evolution.* New York, Holt, 1959.

KRAUS, B. S. and WHITE, C. B.: Micro-evolution in a human population. *Amer. Anthropol., 58:*1017-1043, 1956.

KRAUS, W. W.: Race crossing in Hawaii. *J. Heredity, 32:*371-378, 1941.

KRETSCHMER, E.: *Physique and Character.* New York, Harcourt, 1925.

KROEBER, A. L. and KLUCKHOHN, C.: Culture: A Critical Review of Concepts and Definitions. *Papers of the Peabody Museum of American Archaeology and Ethnology, Harvard University, 47:*viii-223, 1952.

KROGMAN, W. M. (editor): The growth of man. *Tabulae Biologicae, 20:*vi-963, 1942.

———: *A Guide-Outline for the Study of Physical Growth in Children.* Philadelphia, Philadelphia Center for Research in Child Growth, 1958.

———: Changing man. *J. Am. Geriatrics Soc., 6:*242-260, 1958.

———: A Handbook of the Measurement and Interpretation of Height and Weight in the Growing Child. *Mon. Soc. Res. Child. Develop., 8:*1-68, 1950.

———: The human skeleton in legal medicine. In S. A. Levinson (editor): *Symposium on Medicolegal Problems.* Philadelphia, Lippincott, 1949, pp. 1-100.

———: *A Bibliography of Human Morphology, 1914-1939.* Chicago, Univ. Chicago Press, 1941.

KROPOTKIN, P.: *Mutual Aid.* Boston, Porter Sargent, 1955.

KRZYWICKI, L.: *Primitive Society and Its Vital Statistics.* London, Macmillan, 1934.

KUNO, Y.: *Human Perspiration.* Springfield, Thomas, 1956.

KURTÉN, B.: Mammal migrations, Cenozoic stratigraphy, and the age of Peking Man and the Australopithecines. *J. Paleontology, 31:*215-227, 1957.

———: A Case of Darwinian selection in bears. *Evolution, 11:*412-416, 1958.

———: A differentiation index, and a new measure of evolutionary rates. *Evolution, 12:*146-157, 1958.

———: The life and death of the Pleistocene cave bear. *Acta Zoologica Fennica* 95, Helsinki-Helsingfors, 1959, pp. 59.

KURTZ, A. K. and EDGERTON, H. A.: *Statistical Dictionary of Terms and Symbols.* New York, Wiley, 1939.

LACAILLE, A. D.: Châtelperron: a new survey of its palaeolithic industry. *Archaeologia,* 92:95-119, 1947.

————: The stone industry of Singa—Abu Hugar. In *Fossil Mammals of Africa,* No. 2, British Museum (Natural History), 43-50, 1951.

LADELL, W. S. S.: The influence of environment in arid regions on the biology of man. In *Human and Animal Ecology,* UNESCO Publication, Arid Zone Research VIII, New York, Columbia Univ. Press, 1957, 43-99.

LANGER, W. L. (editor): *An Encyclopaedia of World History.* 3rd ed. Boston, Houghton Mifflin, 1952.

LASKER, G. W.: The effects of partial starvation on somatotype. An analysis of material from the Minnesota starvation experiment. *Am. J. Phys. Anthropol.,* n.s. 5:323-341, 1947.

————: Migration and physical differentiation. *Am. J. Phys. Anthropol.,* n.s. 4:273-300, 1946.

————: Mixture and genetic drift in ongoing human evolution. *Am. Anthropol.,* 54:433-436, 1952.

————: Human evolution in contemporary communities. *Southwest. J. Anthropol.,* 4:353-365, 1954.

LAUGHLIN, W. S. (editor). *Papers on the Physical Anthropology of the American Indian.* New York, Viking Fund, 1951.

———— and JØRGENSEN, J. B.: Isolate variation in Greenlandic eskimo crania. *Acta Gen. et Stat. Med.,* 6:3-12, 1956.

———— GRAY, M. P. and HOPKINS, C. E.: Blood group genetics of the Basques of Idaho. *Acta Gen. et. Stat. Med.,* 6:536-548, 1956.

LAWLER, S. D. and LAWLER, L. J.: *Human Blood Groups and Inheritance.* Harvard Univ. Press, Cambridge, Mass, 1957.

LAYRISSE, M.: Anthropological considerations of the Diego (Di^a) antigen. Possible application in the studies of Mongoloid and hybrid populations. *Am. J. Phys. Anthropol.,* n.s. 16:173-186, 1958.

———— and DE LAYRISSE, Z.: Frequency of the new blood group antigen Js^a among South American Indians. *Nature, 184:*640, 1959.

LEAKEY, L. S. B.: *Olduvai Gorge.* New York, Cambridge University Press, 1951.

————: *Adam's Ancestors,* 4th ed. London, Methuen, 1953.

————: A new fossil skull from Eyassi, East Africa. *Nature, 138:*1082, 1936.

————: Recent discoveries at Olduvai Gorge, Tanganyika. *Nature, 181:*1099-1103, 1958.

————: A new fossil skull from Olduvai. *Nature, 184:*491-493, 1959.

LEE, M. M. C., and LASKER, G. W.: The sun-tanning potential of human skin. *Human Biology,* 31:252-260, 1959.

LEHMANN, H.: Haemoglobin and its abnormalities. *Practitioner* (London), 178: 198-214, 1957.

LEROI-GOURHAN, A.: *Prehistoric Man.* New York, Philosophical Library, 1957.

LESSA, W. A.: *An Appraisal of Constitutional Typologies.* American Anthropological Association Memoir, No. 62, 1943.

LEVIN, G.: Racial and inferiority characters in the human brain. *Am. J. Phys. Anthropol.,* 22:345-380, 1937.

LEVINE, P., LAYRISSE, M., ARENDS, T., SISCO, R. D.: The Diego blood factor. *Nature*, 177:40-41, 1956.

LEWIS, J. H.: *The Biology of the Negro*. Chicago, Univ. Chicago Press, 1942.

LEWIS, M., KAITA, H. and CHOWN, B.: The blood groups of a Japanese population. *A. J. Hum. Genetics*, 9:274-283, 1957.

LI, C. C.: *Population Genetics*. Univ. Chicago Press, 1955.

―――: *Introduction to Statistical Inference*. Ann Arbor, Michigan, Edwards Bros., 1957.

LIBBY, W. J.: *Radiocarbon Dating*, 2nd ed. Univ. Chicago Press, 1955.

LINTON, R. (editor): *The Science of Man in the World Crisis*. New York, Columbia Univ. Press, 1944.

――― (editor): *Most of the World: The Peoples of Africa, Latin America, and the East Today*. New York, Columbia Univ. Press, 1949.

LIVINGSTONE, F. B.: Anthropological significance of sickle-cell gene distribution in West Africa. *Am. Anthropol.*, 60:533-562, 1958.

LONGHEM, JR., J. J. VAN: Nomenclature of the rhesus typing sera. *Bull. World Health Organization*, 2:215-225, 1949.

LOTSY, J. P. and GODDIJN, W. A.: Voyages of exploration to judge of the bearing of hybridization upon evolution. I. South Africa. *Genetica*, 10:viii-315, 1928.

LOWIE, R. H.: Intellectual and cultural achievements of human races. In *Scientific Aspects of the Race Problem*, New York, Longmans, 1941, p. 189-249.

―――: *The History of Ethnological Theory*. New York, Farrar & Rinehart, 1937.

LUGG, J. W. H.: Taste thresholds for phenylthiocarbamide of some populations. *Ann. Hum. Genetics*, 21:244-253, 1957.

MACALISTER, R. A. S.: *A Textbook of European Archaeology*. Cambridge and New York, Cambridge Univ. Press, 1921.

MACCURDY, G. G.: *Human Origins*, 2 vols. New York, Appleton, 1924.

――― (editor): *Early Man*. Philadelphia, Lippincott, 1930.

MACGOWAN, K.: *Early Man in the New World*. New York, Macmillan, 1950.

MACINNES, D. G.: Notes on the East African Miocene primates. *J. East Africa Uganda Natur. Hist. Soc.*, 18:141-148, 1943.

MCBURNEY, C. B.: *The Stone Age of Northern Africa*. Baltimore, Md., Penguin Books, 1959.

――― TREVOR, J. C. and WELLS, L. H.: The Haua-Fteah fossil jaw. *J. Roy. Anthropol. Inst.*, 83:71-85, 1953.

MCCOWN, T. D. and KEITH, A.: *The Stone Age of Mount Carmel*. Oxford, The Clarendon Press, 1939.

MACY, I. G. and KELLY, H. J.: *Chemical Anthropology*. Univ. Chicago Press, 1957.

M'GONIGLE, G. C. M. and KIRBY, J.: *Poverty and Public Health*. London, Victor Gollancz, 1936.

MAINLAND, D.: *Elementary Medical Statistics*. Philadelphia, Saunders, 1952.

MALEZ, M.: Die Höhle Veternica, eine neue paläolithische Fundstelle in Kroatien. *Bull. Scient.* (Jugoslavia), 3:11, 1956.

MANUILA, A.: Recherches sérologiques et anthropologiques ches les populations de la Roumanie et des régions voisines: Contribution a l'étude du problème Dinarique. *Arch. Jul. Klaus-Stiftung f. Vererbungsf. Sozialanthropolo. u. Rassenhygiene*, 32:219-357.

————: Blood groups and disease—hard facts and delusions. *J.A.M.A., 167:* 2047-2053, 1958.

MARDER, V. J., and CONLEY, C. L.: Electrophoresis of hemoglobin on agar gels. *Bull. Johns Hopkins Hosp., 105:*77-88, 1959.

MARTIN, H.: *The Sheltering Desert.* New York, Nelson, 1958.

MARTIN, R.: *Lehrbuch der Anthropologie,* 2nd edition, 3 vols. Jena, Fischer, 1928. Third edition edited by Karl Saller, began to appear in parts, issued by the same publisher, in 1956.

MATUS, S.: The mongol spot in the Cape Coloured. *S. Afr. Med. J.,* 12 April 1941.

MAY, J. M.: *The Ecology of Human Disease.* New York, MD Publications, 1959.

MAYR, E.: *Systematics and the Origin of Species.* New York, Columbia Univ. Press, 1942.

————: Taxonomic categories in fossil hominids. *Cold Spring Harbor Symposia on Quantitative Biology, 15:*109-118, 1950.

———— (editor): *The Species Problem.* Washington, D.C. American Association for the Advancement of Science, 1957.

———— LINSLEY, G. E. and USINGER, R. L.: *Methods and Principles of Systematic Zoology.* New York, McGraw-Hill, 1953.

MEGGERS, B. J. (editor): *Evolution and Anthropology: A Centennial Appraisal.* Washington, D.C., The Anthropological Society of Washington, 1959.

MEREDITH, H. V.: Relation between socioeconomic status and body size in boys seven to ten years of age. *Am. J. Dis. Child., 82:*702-709, 1951.

MERRITT, E. L.: *Analytical Photogrammetry.* New York, Pitman, 1958.

MERTON, B. B.: Taste sensitivity to PTC. *Acta Genetica et Statistica Medica, 8:* 114-128, 1958.

MERTON, R. K., and MONTAGU, M. F. ASHLEY: Crime and the anthropologist. *Am. Anthropol., 42:*384-408, 1940.

METTLER, F. A.: *Culture and the Structural Evolution of the Nervous System.* New York, American Museum of Natural History, 1956.

MEWHINNEY, H.: *A Manual for Neanderthals.* Austin, Univ. Texas, 1957.

MIDDLETON, J.: On fluorine in bones, its source, and its application to the determination of the geological age of fossil bones. *Proc. Geol. Soc. Lond., 4:*431-433, 1844.

MILLER, JR., G. S.: The controversy over human "missing links." *Smithsonian Report for 1928,* Smithsonian Institution, Washington, D.C., 1929, 413-465.

MOHR, J.: Taste sensitivity to phenylthiourea in Denmark. *Ann. Hum. Genetics,* 21:282-286, 1957.

MONGE, C.: *Acclimatization in the Andes.* Baltimore, Johns Hopkins Press, 1948.

————: Biological basis of behavior. In A. L. Kroeber (editor): *Anthropology Today.* Univ. Chicago Press, 1953, 127-144.

MONTAGU, M. F. ASHLEY: A cursory examination of the relations between physical and social anthropology. *Am. J. Phys. Anthropol., 26:*41-61, 1940.

————: *Edward Tyson, M.D., F.R.S. (1650-1708): and the Rise of Human and Comparative Anatomy in England.* Philadelphia, American Philosophical Society, 1943.

————: The intelligence of northern Negroes and southern whites in the first World War. *Am. J. Psychol., 48:*161-188, 1945.

————: On the relation between body size, waking activity, and the origin of social life in the primates. *Am. Anthropol., 44:*141-145, 1944.

————: Physical anthropology and anatomy. *Am. J. Phys. Anthropol.*, 27:261-271, 1941.

————: The premaxilla in the primates. *Quart. Rev. Biol.*, 10:32-59, 181-208, 1935.

————: The premaxilla in man. *J. Am. Dent. A.*, 23:2043-2057, 1936.

————: The medio-frontal suture and the problem of metopism in the primates. *J. Roy. Anthropol. Inst.*, 67:157-201, 1937.

————: Genetics and the antiquity of man in the Americas. *Man*, 43:131-135, 1943.

————: *Man's Most Dangerous Myth: The Fallacy of Race*, 3rd edition. New York, Harper, 1952.

————: The tarsian hypothesis and the descent of man. *J. Roy. Anthropol. Inst.*, 60:335-362, 1930.

————: The origin and nature of social life and the biological basis of cooperation. *J. Soc. Psychol.*, 29:267-283, 1949.

————: *On Being Human.* New York, Schuman, 1950.

————: *Darwin, Competition, and Cooperation.* New York, Schuman, 1952.

————: *The Natural Superiority of Women.* New York, Macmillan, 1953.

————: The Barcombe Mills cranial remains. *Am. J. Phys. Anthropol.*, n.s. 9:417-426, 1951.

————: The Piltdown mandible and cranium. *Am. J. Phys. Anthropol.*, n.s. 9:464-470, 1951.

————: The Piltdown nasal turbinate and bone implement: some questions. *Science*, 119:884-886, 1954.

————: Time, morphology, and neoteny in the evolution of man. *Amer. Anthropol.*, 57:13-27, 1955.

————: The Kanam mandible. *Amer. Anthropol.*, 59:335-339, 1957.

————: Neoteny, and the evolution of the human mind. *Explorations* (University of Toronto), No. 6, 85-90, 1956.

————: The Natchez innominate bone. *Human Biology*, 27:193-201, 1955.

————: *The Direction of Human Development.* New York, Harper, 1955.

————: *Anthropology and Human Nature.* Boston, Porter, Sargent, 1957.

————: *The Reproductive Development of the Female.* New York, Julian Press, 1957.

————: *Human Heredity.* New York, World Publishing Co., 1959.

————: *Man: His First Million Years.* New York, New American Library, 1958.

———— and MERTON, R. K.: Crime and the anthropologist. *Am. Anthropol.*, 42:384-408, 1940.

———— and OAKLEY, K. P.: The antiquity of Galley Hill man. *Am. J. Phys. Anthropol.*, n.s. 7:363-384, 1949.

———— STEEN, E. S.: *Anatomy and Physiology*, 2 vols. New York, Barnes & Noble, 1959.

MONTOYE, H. J.: *The Longevity and Morbidity of College Athletes.* Phi Epsilon Fraternity, Indianapolis, Indiana, 1957.

MOOR-JANKOWSKI, J. K.: La prépondérance du groupe sanguin O et du facteur Rhésus négatif chez les Walser de Suisse. *J. Gén. Hum.*, 3:25-70, 1954.

———— and HUSER, H. J.: Seroanthropological investigations in the Walser and Romanish isolates of the Swiss Alps. Proc. 6th Congr. Interna. Soc. Blood Transf., Boston, 1956, *Bibl. Haem.*, 7:215-219, 1958.

MORANT, G. M.: *The Races of Central Europe.* New York, Norton, 1939.

————: Studies of Palaeolithic Man. *Ann. Eugenics, 1:*257-276, 1926; *2:*318-381, 1927; *3:*337-360; *4:*109-214, 1930.

————: The practical application of physical anthropology. *Zeit. f. Morph. u. Anthropol., 119:*196-204, 1958.

MORONEY, M. G.: *Facts from Figures.* Baltimore, Penguin Books, 1951.

MOULLEC, J. and FINE, J. M.: Frequencies of the haptoglobin groups in 406 French blood donors. *Nature, 184:*196-197, 1959.

MOURANT, A. E.: *The Distribution of the Human Blood Groups.* Springfield, Thomas, 1954.

————: Blood groups and human evolution. *Proc. Brit. A. Adv. Sci.,* No. 50, 1956, 1-13.

————: *The ABO Blood Groups.* Springfield, Thomas, 1958.

MOVIUS, JR., H. L.: Lower paleolithic archaeology in Southern Asia and the Far East. In *Early Man in the Far East* (edited by W. W. Howells), p. 17-81, Philadelphia, The Wistar Institute, 1949.

————: Palaeolithic archaeology in Southern and Eastern Asia, exclusive of India. *J. World Hist., 2:*258-282, 520-553, 1955.

MULLER, H. J., LITTLE, C. C. and SNYDER, L. H.: *Genetics, Medicine, and Man.* Ithaca, New York, Cornell Univ. Press, 1947.

MYRDAL, G.: *An American Dilemma: The Negro Problem and American Democracy.* 2 vols. New York, Harper, 1944.

NABOURS, R. K.: Emergent evolution and hybridism. *Science, 71:*371-375, 1930.

NASMYTH, G.: *Social Progress and the Darwinian Theory.* New York, Putnam, 1916.

NEGUS, V.: *The Comparative Anatomy and Physiology of the Nose and Paranasal Sinuses.* Baltimore, Williams & Wilkins, 1958.

NEWMAN, H. H.: *Multiple Human Births.* New York, Doubleday, Doran, 1940.

————, FREEMAN, F. N. and HOLZINGER, K. H.: *Twins: A Study of Heredity and Environment.* Chicago, Univ. Chicago Press, 1937.

NEWMAN, M. T.: The application of ecological rules to the racial anthropology of the aboriginal New World. *Amer. Anthropol., 55:*309-327, 1955.

NISSEN, H. W.: A field study of the Chimpanzee. *Compt. Psychol. Monogr., 8:* serial no. 36, 1931.

Notes and Queries on Anthropology, 6th ed. London, Routledge, 1951.

NYMAN, M.: Über Haptoglobinbestimmung im Serum, Normalkonzentration und Verhaltnis zu Smithies Serumgruppen. *Clin. Chim. Acta, 3:*111, 1958.

OAKLEY, K. P.: A definition of man. *Science News* (London), Penguin Books, No. 20, May 1951, 68-81.

————: Tools or brains—which came first? *The Listener* (London), Dec. 19, 1957, 1027-1028.

————: The earliest tool-makers and the earliest fire-makers. *Antiquity, 30:*4-8, 1-2-107, 1956.

————: *Man the Tool-Maker,* 4th ed. London, British Museum (Natural History), 1958. Chicago, Univ. Chicago Press, 1958.

————: Dating fossil men. *Mem. & Proc. Manchester Lit. & Phil. Soc., 98:* 1-18, 1956/57.

————: Swanscombe man. *Proc. Geol. Assoc., 63:*271-300, 1952.

———— and HOSKINS, C. R.: New evidence on the antiquity of Piltdown Man. *Nature, 165:*379-382, 1950.

———— and MONTAGU, M. F. ASHLEY: A reconsideration of the Galley Hill skeleton. *Bull. Brit. Museum Natur. Hist.*, 1:25-48, 1949.

OLIVER, J. A., MACKAY, I., and GOT, C.: Serum haptoglobins in hepatobiliary disease. *Brit. M. J.*, 1:1454-1456, 1959.

OLIVIER, G. and PINEAU, H.: Détermination du sexe par le poids des os. *Bull. et Mém. de la Soc. d'Anthrop. Paris*, 9:329-339, 1958.

OLSON, E. C. and MILLER, R. C.: *Morphological Integration.* Univ. Chicago Press, 1958.

OTTENSOOSER, F.: Blood groups, races and prehistory. *Hum. Biol.*, 27:253-257, 1955.

OWEN, J. A., MACKAY, I., and GOT, C.: Haptoglobins in hepatobiliary disease. *Br. Med. J.*, 1:1454-1456, 1959.

PARNELL, R. W.: *Behavior and Physique.* London, Arnold, 1958.

PATERSON, D. G.: *Physique and Intellect.* New York, Century Co., 1930.

PATTE, É.: *Les Neanderthaliens.* Paris, Masson, 1955.

PATTEN, W.: *The Grand Strategy of Evolution.* Boston, Badger, 1920.

PATTERSON, B.: The geologic history of the non-hominid primates in the Old World. *Hum. Biol.*, 26:191-209, 1954.

PEACOCK, L. J. and ROGERS, C. M.: Gestation period and twinning in chimpanzees. *Science*, 129:959, 1959.

PEARL, R.: *Introduction to Medical Biometry and Statistics*, 3rd edition, Philadelphia, Saunders, 1940.

————: *The Rate of Living.* New York, Knopf, 1928.

————: The search for longevity. *Scient. Monthly*, 46:462-483, 1938.

———— and MOFFET, E. W.: Bodily constitution and human longevity. *Proc. Nat. Acad. Sciences*, 25:609-616, 1939.

————: *Man the Animal.* Bloomington, Indiana, Principia Press, 1946.

PEARSON, K.: Relationship of intelligence to size and shape of the head and other mental and physical characters. *Biometrika*, 5:105-106, 1906.

PEI, W. C.: Giant ape's jaw bone discovered in China. *Amer. Anthropol.*, 59: 834-838, 1957.

PENNIMAN, T. K.: *A Hundred Years of Anthropology*, 2nd ed. New York, Macmillan, 1952.

PERLA, D. and MARMORSTON, J.: *Natural Resistance and Clinical Medicine.* Baltimore, Williams & Wilkins, 1941.

PETERSEN, W. R.: *The Patient and the Weather*, 4 vols. Ann Arbor, Michigan, Edwards Bros., 1934-1938.

PIGGOTT, S.: *Approach to Archaeology.* London, Black, 1959.

PIVETEAU, J.: *Primates et Paléontologie Humaine. Traité De Paléontologie*, 7: 1-657. Paris, Masson et Cie., 1957.

PONS, J.: Taste sensitivity to phenylthiourea in Spaniards. *Hum. Biol.*, 27:153-160, 1955.

QUENSTEDT, W. and A.: *Fossilium Catalogus. Hominidae Fossiles.* 's-Gravenhague, Funk, 1936.

RANSON, S. W.: *The Anatomy of the Nervous System*, 7th edition. Philadelphia, Saunders, 1939.

RAO, C. R.: *Advanced Statistical Methods in Biometrical Research.* New York, Wiley, 1952.

REID, R. R. and MULLIGAN, H. H.: Relation of cranial capacity to intelligence. *J. Roy. Anthropol. Inst.*, 53:322-332, 1923.

RIFE, D. C.: *Dice of Destiny*, 2nd ed. Columbus, Ohio, Long's College Book Co., 1947.

ROBERTS, D. F.: Body weight, race and climate. *Am. J. Phys. Anthropol.*, n.s. 11:533-558, 1953.

————: Basal metabolism, race and climate. *J. Roy. Anthropol. Inst.*, 82:169-183, 1952.

————: An ecological approach to physical anthropology. *Actes Congr. IV Internat. Sci. Anthropol. et Ethnol.*, 1:145-148, 1952

ROBERTS, D. F. and WEINER, J. S. (editors): *The Scope of Physical Anthropology and its Place in Academic Studies.* London, Institute for Biology, 1958.

ROBERTS, J. A.: Surnames and blood groups, with a note on a probable remarkable difference between North and South Wales. *Nature, 149*:138, 1942.

ROBERTS, J. FRASER: *An Introduction to Medical Genetics,* 2nd ed. New York, Oxford Univ. Press, 1959.

————: The contribution of genetics to physical anthropology. *J. Roy. Anthrop. Inst., 88*:115-129, 1958.

ROBINSON, J. T.: Telanthropus and its phylogenetic significance. *Am. J. Phys. Anthropol.*, n.s. II:445-501, 1953.

————: *The Dentition of the Australopithecinae.* Transvaal Museum Memoir No. 9, Transvaal Museum, Pretoria, 1956.

————: Occurrence of stone artefacts with Australopithecus at Sterkfontein. *Nature, 180*:521-524, 1957.

————: A bone implement from Sterkfontein. *Nature, 184*:583-585, 1959.

————: Cranial cresting patterns and their significance in the Hominoidea. *Am. J. Phys. Anthropol.*, n.s. 16:397-428, 1959.

RODENWALDT, E.: *Die Mestizen auf Kisar,* 2 vols. Batavia, 1927.

ROE, A. and SIMPSON, G. G. (editors): *Evolution and Behavior.* New Haven, Yale Univ. Press, 1958.

ROMER, A. S.: *Man and the Vertebrates,* 4th ed. Baltimore, Penguin Books, 1958.

ROWAN, W.: *The Riddle of Migration.* Baltimore, Williams & Wilkins, 1931.

ROWE, C. W.: Genetics vs. physical anthropology in determining racial types. *Southwest. J. Anthropol.*, 2:197-211, 1950.

RUCH, T. C.: *Bibliographica Primatologica.* Springfield, Thomas, 1941.

————: *Diseases of Laboratory Primates.* Philadelphia, Saunders, 1959.

SALDANHA, P. H.: Taste thresholds for phenylthiourea among Japanese. *Ann. Hum. Genetics, 22*:380-384, 1958.

SANDERS, B. S.: *Environment and Growth.* Baltimore, Warwick & York, 1934.

SCHEINFELD, A.: *The New You and Heredity.* Philadelphia, Lippincott, 1950.

————: *Women and Men.* New York, Harcourt, 1944.

————: The mortality of men and women. *Scientific American, 198*:22-28, 1958.

SCHENKE, E. T. and McMASTERS, J. H.: *Procedures in Taxonomy,* 3rd ed. California, Stanford Univ. Press, 1956.

SCHULTZ, A. H.: Fetal growth of man and other primates. *Quart. Rev. Biol., 1*: 493-495, 1926.

————: The skeleton of the trunk and limbs of higher primates. *Human Biol., 2*: 381-383, 1930.

————: Die Körperproportionen der erwachsenen Primaten, mit spezieller Berücksichtigung der Menschenaffen. *Anthropol. Anz., 10*:154-185, 1933.

————: Characters common to higher primates and characters specific for man. *Quart. Rev. Biol., 11*:259-283, 425-455, 1936.

————: Ontogenetic specializations of man. *Arch. Julius Klaus-Stiftung, 24*: 197-216, 1949.

————: Die Bedeutung der Primatenkunde für das Verstandnis der Anthropogenese. *Deut. Ges. f. Anthropol.*, 13-28, Gottingen, 1957.

————: Past and present views of man's specializations. *Irish J. Med. Sc.*, 341-356, 1957.

————: The physical distinctions of man. *Proc. Am. Phil. Soc.*, 94:428-449, 1950.

SCHWESINGER, G. C.: *Heredity and Environment.* New York, Holt, 1930.

SCOTT, E. M., GRIFFITH, I. V. and HOSKINS, D. D.: Lack of abnormal hemoglobins in Alaskans Eskimos, Indians, and Aleuts. *Science, 129:*719-720, 1959.

SCOTT, J. H.: The variability of cranial and facial dimensions in modern skulls. *Brit. Dent. J., 94:*27-31, 1953.

SELIGMAN, C. G.: *Races of Africa*, 3rd ed. New York, Oxford Univ. Press, 1957.

SELLARDS, E. H.: *Early Man in America.* Austin, Univ. Texas Press, 1952.

SEMPLE, N. M., SIMMONS, R. T. and GRAYDON, J. J.: Blood group frequencies in natives of the Central Highlands of New Guinea, and in the Bainings of New Britain. *Med. J. Austral.*, 365, 371, Sept. 8, 1956.

SHAPIRO, H. L.: Descendants of the mutineers of the bounty. *Mem. Bernice P. Bishop Museum* (Honolulu), 9:1-106, 1929.

————: *The Heritage of the Bounty.* New York, Simon & Schuster, Inc., 1936.

———— and HULSE, F.: *Migration and Environment.* New York, Oxford Univ. Press, 1940.

SHELDON, W. H.: *The Varieties of Human Physique.* New York, Harper, 1940.

————: *The Varieties of Human Temperament.* New York, Harper, 1942.

————: *Varieties of Delinquent Youth.* New York, Harper, 1949.

————: *Atlas of Men.* New York, Harper, 1954.

SHEPHERD, R. H., SHOLL, D. A. and VIZOZO, A.: The size relationship subsisting between body length, limbs and jaws in man. *J. Anat.*, 83:296-302, 1949.

SHERRINGTON, C.: *Man on His Nature.* New York, Macmillan, 1941.

SHETTLES, L. B.: Biological sex differences with special reference to disease, resistance, and longevity. *J. Obst. & Gynaec. Brit. Emp.*, 45:288-295, 1958.

SIMMONS, R. T., GRAYDON, J. J. and SRINGAM, S.: A blood group genetical survey in Thais, Bangkok. *Am. J. Phys. Anthropol.*, n.s. 12:407-412, 1954.

————: GRAYDON, J. J. and SEMPLE, N. M.: A blood group genetical survey in Australian aborigines. *Am. J. Phys. Anthropol.*, n.s. 12:599-606, 1954.

————: GRAYDON, J. J., SEMPLE, N. M., and FRY, E. I.: A blood group genetical survey in Cook Islanders, Polynesia, and comparisons with American Indians. *Am. J. Phys. Anthropol.*, n.s. 13:667-690, 1955.

————: GRAYDON, J. J., SEMPLE, N. M. and SWINDLER, D. R.: A blood group genetical survey in West Nakanai, New Britain. *Am. J. Phys. Anthropol.*, n.s. 14:275-286, 1956.

———— and GRAYDON, J. J.: A blood group genetical survey in Eastern and Central Polynesians. *Am. J. Phys. Anthropol.*, 15:357-366, 1957.

————, SEMPLE, N. M., CLELAND, J. B. and CASLEY-SMITH, J. R.: A blood group genetical survey in Australian aborigines at Haast's Bluff, Central Australia. *Am. J. Phys. Anthropol.*, 15:547-554, 1957.

SIMPSON, G. G.: The principles of classification and a classification of mammals. *Bull. Am. Museum Natur. Hist.*, 85:xvi-350, 1945.

————: *The Major Features of Evolution.* New York, Columbia Univ. Press, 1953.

————: *The Meaning of Evolution.* New Haven, Yale Univ. Press, 1949.

————, PITTENDRIGH, C. S. and TIFFANY, L. H.: *An Introduction to Biology.* New York, Harcourt Brace, 1957.

————, ROE, A. and LEWONTIN, R. C.: *Quantitative Zoology.* New York, Mc-Graw-Hill, 1960.

SINGER, R.: The Saldanha skull from Hopefield, South Africa. *Amer. J. Phys. Anthropol.*, n.s. 12:346-362, 1954.

————: The Boskop "race" problem. *Man*, 58:173-178, 1958.

SKERLJ, B.: The role and position of Neanderthal man in human evolution. *Acta Archaeologica*, 8:347-368, 1956.

————: Were Neanderthalers the only inhabitants of Krapina? *Bulletin Scientifique*, 4:44, 1958.

SMITH, G. ELLIOT: *The Evolution of Man*, 2nd edition. New York, Oxford, 1927.

SMITHIES, O.: Zone electrophoresis in starch gels: group variations in the serum proteins of normal human adults. *Biochem. J.*, 61:629, 1955.

————: Variation in human serum β-globulins. *Nature*, 180:1482-83, 1957.

SNEDECOR, G. W.: *Statistical Methods*, 5th edition. Ames, Iowa, Collegiate Press, 1956.

SNYDER, L. H.: The effects of selection and domestication on man. *J. Nat. Cancer. Inst.*, 15:759-769, 1954.

————: Fifty years of medical genetics. *Science*, 129:7-13, 1959.

SNYDER, L. L.: *Race.* Chicago, Ziff-Davis, 1939.

SONNTAG, C. F.: *The Morphology of the Apes and Man.* London, Bale, 1924.

SORSBY, A. (editor): *Clinical Genetics.* St. Louis, Mosby, 1953.

SPIER, L.: Growth of Japanese children born in America and in Japan. *Univ. Washington Pub. Anthropol.*, 3: 1929.

SPUHLER, J. N.: An estimate of the number of genes in man. *Science*, 108:279, 1948.

SPUHLER, J. N. (editor): The evolution of man's capacity for culture. *Human Biology*, 31:1-73, 1959.

———— and KLUCKHOHN, C.: Inbreeding coefficients of the Ramah Navaho population. *Hum. Biol.*, 25:295-317, 1953.

STEGGERDA, M.: The inheritance of hair form. *Eugenical News*, 16:56-57, 1931.

————: *The Maya Indians of Yucatan.* Washington, Carnegie Inst., Publication 531, 1941.

STEIN, L.: *The Infancy of Speech and the Speech of Infancy.* London, Methuen, 1949.

STERN, B. J.: *Society and Medical Progress.* Princeton, Princeton Univ. Press, 1941.

STERN, C.. *Principles of Human Genetics.* 2nd ed. San Francisco, Freeman, 1960.

————: The problem of complete Y-linkage in man. *Am. J. Hum. Genetics,* **9:** 147-166, 1957.

STEWARD, J. H. (editor): *Handbook of South American Indians.* Washington, D.C., Bureau of American Ethnology, 1945-50, 6 vols.

———— and FARON, L. C. (editors): *Native Peoples of South America.* New York, McGraw-Hill, 1959.

STEWART, T. D.: Antiquity of man in America demonstrated by the fluorine test. *Science, 113:*391-392, 1951.

STIRTON, R. A.: *Time, Life and Man.* New York, Wiley, 1959.

STRANDSKOV, H. H.: The distribution of human genes. *Scientific Monthly, 52:* 203-215, 1942.

————: The genetics of human populations. *Am. Naturalist, 76:*156-164, 1942.

STRATTON, F. and RENTON, P. H.: *Practical Blood Grouping.* Springfield, Thomas, 1959.

STRAUS, JR., W. L.: The riddle of man's ancestry. *Quart. Rev. Biol.,* 24:200-223, 1949.

————: Pithecanthropus in Africa. *Science, 123:*498, 1956.

————: Oreopithecus bambolii. *Science, 126:*345-346, 1957.

————: Saldanha man and his culture. *Science, 125:*973-974, 1957.

———— and CAVE, A. J. E.: Pathology and posture of Neanderthal man. *Quart. Rev. Biol.,* 32:348-363, 1957.

STRONG, L. C., *et al.*: Parental age and characteristics of the offspring. *Ann. N. Y. Acad. Sc.,* 57:453-613, 1954.

STUCKERT, R. J.: African ancestry of the white American population. *Ohio J. Sci.,* 58:155-160, 1958.

STURTEVANT, W. C.: *Anthropology as a Career.* Washington, D.C., Smithsonian Institution, 1958.

SULLIVAN, L. R.: The pygmy races of man. *Natur. Hist.,* 19:687-695, 1919.

————: *Essentials of Anthropometry. A handbook for Explorers and Museum Collectors.* New York, American Museum of Natural History, 1928.

SUNDERMAN, F. W. and BOERNER, F.: *Normal Values in Clinical Medicine.* Philadelphia, Saunders, 1959.

SUSSMAN, L. N., MEYER, L. H. and CONARD, R. A.: Blood groupings in Marshallese. *Science, 129:*644-645, 1958.

SUTTON, H. E., *et al.*: Serum protein differences between Africans and Caucasians. *Nature, 178:*1287, 1956.

SWANSCOMBE COMMITTEE: Report on the Swanscombe skull. *J. Roy. Anthropol. Inst.,* 58:17-98, 1938.

SYMPOSIUM: *Origin and Evolution of Man.* Cold Spring Harbor, L.I., *Cold Spring Harbor Symposia on Quantitative Biology,* XV:vii-425, 1950.

SZILARD, L.: On the nature of the aging process. *Proc. Nat. Acad. Sci.,* 45: 30-45, 1959.

TANNER, J. M.: *Growth at Adolescence.* Springfield, Thomas, 1955.

TAX, S., *et al.*: *An Appraisal of Anthropology Today.* Univ. Chicago Press, 1953.

THAMBIPILLAI, V.: Taste threshold for thiophenyl-urea in Malay school children. *Ann. Eug.,* 20:232-238, 1956.

THIEME, F. P.: The geographic and racial distribution of ABO and Rh blood types and tasters of PTC in Puerto Rico. *Am. J. Hum. Genetics,* 4:94-112, 1952.

THOMA, A.: Métissage ou transformation? Essai sur les hommes fossiles de Palestine. *L'Anthropologie*, 61:470-502, 1957; 62:30-52, 1958.

THOMAS, JR., W. L. (editor): *Man's Role in Changing The Face of the Earth*. Univ. Chicago, Press, 1956.

THOMPSON, A. and BUXTON, L. H. D.: Man's nasal index in relation to certain climatic conditions. *J. Roy. Anthropol. Inst.*, 53:92-122, 1923.

THOMPSON, CHARLES H. (editor): The physical and mental abilities of the American Negro. *J. Negro Education*, 3:317-564, 1934.

THOMPSON, E. T. (editor): *Race Relations and the Race Problem*. Durham, N.C., Duke Univ. Press, 1939.

THORNDIKE, E. L.: *Human Nature and the Social Order*. New York, Macmillan, 1940.

TINDALE, N. B.: Survey of the half-caste problem in South Australia. *Proc. Roy. Geographical Soc., South Australian Branch*, Session 1940-1941, p. 66-161.

TJIO, J. H. and PUCK, T. T.: The somatic chromosomes of man. *Proc. Nat. Acad. Sci.*, 44:1229-1237, 1958.

TOBIAS, P. V.: On a Bushman-European hybrid family. *Man*, No. 287, 1-4, 1954.

———: Les Boschimans Auen et Naron de Ghanzi. *L'Anthropologie*, 59/60:235 sq, 1955/56.

———: On the survival of the Bushman. *Africa*, 26:174-186, 1956.

———: Some aspects of the biology of the Bantu-speaking African. *The Leech*, pp. 3-12, Aug. 1958.

———: Physical anthropology and somatic origins of the Hottentots. *African Studies*, 14:1-15, 1955.

TODD, T. WINGATE: Cranial capacity and linear dimensions. *Am. J. Phys. Anthropol.*, 6:97-194, 1923.

——— and LINDALA, A.: Dimensions of the body, whites and American Negroes of both sexes. *Am. J. Phys. Anthropol.*, 12:35-119, 1928.

——— and LYON, D. W.: Cranial suture closure; its progress and age relationship. Part IV. Ectocranial closure in adult males of Negro stock. *Am. J. Phys. Anthropol.*, 8:149-168, 1925.

——— and GORDOR, L. VAN: The quantitative determination of black pigmentation in the skin of the American Negro. *Am. J. Phys. Anthropol.*, 4:239-260, 1921.

——— et al.: The color top method of recording skin pigmentation. *Am. J. Phys. Anthropol.*, 11:187-204, 1928.

TROTTER, M.: Hair growth and shaving. *Anat. Rec.*, 37:373-379, 1928.

——— and GLESTER, G. C.: Estimation of stature from long bones of American whites and Negroes. *Am. J. Phys. Anthropol.*, n.s. 10:463-514, 1952.

TUCKER, W. B. and LESSA, W. A.: Man: a constitutional investigation. *Quart. Rev. Biol.*, 15:265-289, 1940.

TURNER, R.: *The Great Cultural Traditions*, 2 vols. New York, McGraw-Hill, 1941.

VALLOIS, H. V.: The Fontéchevade fossil men. *Am. J. Phys. Anthropol.*, n.s. 7: 339-362, 1949.

———: La mandibule humaine fossile de la Grotte du Porc-Epic près. Dire-Daoua (Abyssinie). *L'Anthropol.*, 55:231-238, 1951.

———: La capacité cranienne cher les Primates supérieurs et le "Rubicon cérébral. C.r. des Sci. de l'Acad. des Sci., 238:1349-1351, 1954.

————: The pre-Mousterian human mandible from Montmaurin. *Amer. J. Phys. Anthropol.,* n.s., *14:*319-323, 1956.

————: Neanderthals and praesapiens. *J. Roy. Anthropol. Inst., 84:*111-130, 1954.

————: La Grotte de Fontéchevade. Pt. 2. Anthropologie. *Arch. l'Inst. Pal. Hum., Paris,* Memoire No. 29, 5-164, 1958.

———— and Movius, Jr., H. (editors): *Catalogue Des Hommes Fossiles.* XIXᵉ Congrès Géologique International, Faculté des Sciences, Alger, French North Africa, 1952.

Voss, H.: *Bibliographie des Menschenaffen (Schimpanse, Orang, Gorilla).* Jena, Fischer, 1955.

Waddington, C. H.: *The Strategy of the Genes.* New York, Macmillan, 1957.

Walker, E. P.: *The Monkey Book.* New York, Macmillan, 1954.

Wallace, B.: Genetic studies of population. *Eugenics Quart., 1:*10-15, 1954.

———— and Dobzhansky, Th.: *Radiation, Genes, and Man.* Holt, 1959.

Wallis, W. D.: *Culture and Progress.* New York, Whittlesey House, 1930.

————: Variability in race hybrids. *Am. Anthropol., 40:*680-697, 1938.

Washburn, S. L.: Thinking about race. *Science Education, 28:*65-76, 1944.

————: Sex differences in the pubic bone. *Am. J. Phys. Anthropol.,* n.s. 7:425-432, 1949.

————: Australopithecines: the hunters or the hunted? *Amer. Anthropol., 59:* 612-614, 1957.

————: The new physical anthropology. *Trans. N.Y. Acad. Sc., 13:*298-304, 1951.

Watson, E. H. and Lowrey, G. H.: *Growth and Development of Children,* 3rd ed. Chicago, Year Book Pub., 1959.

Weckler, J. E.: The relations between Neanderthal man and *Homo sapiens. Amer. Anthropol., 56:*1003-1025, 1954.

Weidenreich, F.: Some problems dealing with ancient man. *Am. Anthropol., 42:* 373-383, 1940.

————: The "Neanderthal man" and the ancestors of *"Homo sapiens." Am. Anthropologist, 45:*39-48, 1943.

————: The skull of Sinanthropus Pekinensis: a comparative study on a primitive hominid skull. *Palaeontologica Sinica,* n.s., D, whole series, No. 127, 1943.

————: The Keilor skull: A Wadjak type from Southeast Australia. *Am. J. Phys. Anthropol.,* n.s. 3:21-32, 1945.

————: Giants and early man from Java and South China. *Anthropol. Papers Am. Museum Nat. Hist., 40: 1;* 1-134, 1945, New York.

————: The paleolithic child from the Teshik-Tash cave in Southern Uzbekistan (Central Asia). *Am. J. Phys. Anthropol.,* n.s., *3:*151-163, 1945.

————: *Apes, Giants, and Man.* Chicago, Univ. Chicago Press, 1946.

————: The trend of human evolution. *Evolution, 1:*221-236, 1947.

————: Interpretations of the fossil material. In *Early Man In the Far East* (edited by W. W. Howells), p. 149-157, Philadelphia, The Wistar Institute, 1949.

————: *Anthropological Papers of Franz Weidenreich 1939-1948.* (Compiled by S. L. Washburn and D. Wolffson.) New York, The Viking Fund, Inc., 1950.

————: Morphology of Solo Man. *Anthropol. Papers Am. Mus. Nat. His., 43:* 205-290, 1951.

Weiner, J. S.: *The Piltdown Forgery.* New York, Oxford Univ. Press, 1955.

————: Nose shape and climate. *Am. J. Phys. Anthropol.*, n.s., *12*:1-3, 1954.

———— and ZOUTENDYK, A.: Blood-group investigation on Central Kalahari Bushmen. *Nature, 183*:843-844, 1959.

———— *et al.*: Further contributions to the solution of the Piltdown problem. *Bull. Brit. Mus. (Nat. Hist.), 2*:227-287, 1955.

————, OAKLEY, K. P. and CLARK, W. E. LE GROS: The solution of the Piltdown problem. *Bull. Brit. Mus. (Nat. Hist.), 2*:141-146, 1953.

WEINERT, H.: Africanthropus, der neue Affenmenschfund in Ostafrika. *Ztschr. Morphol. u. Anthropol.*, 38:18-24, 1939.

WELLS, L. H.: The fossil human skull from Singa. In *Fossil Mammals of Africa*, No. 2, British Museum (Natural History), 1951, 29-42.

————: The Border Cave Skull. *Am. J. Phys. Anthropol.*, n.s., 8:241-243, 1950.

————: 'Human,' 'Hominine,' 'Hominid.' *Man*, 59:30-31, 1959.

WENDORF, F., KRIEGER, A. D., ALBRITTON, C. C. and STEWART, T. D.: *The Midland Discovery.* Austin, Univ. Texas Press, 1955.

WENDT, H.: *In Search of Adam.* Boston, Houghton Mifflin, 1956.

WHITE, L.: The concept of culture. *Am. Anthropol., 61*:227-251, 1959.

WHYTE, L. L.: *The Next Development in Man.* New York, Holt, 1948.

————: *The Unitary Principle in Physics and Biology*, Holt, 1949.

WIENER, A. S.: The Rh factor and racial origins. *Science, 96*:407-408, 1939.

————: *Blood Groups and Transfusion.* Springfield, Thomas, 1943.

————: Rh Glossary. *Laboratory Digest*, p. 1-6, May, 1949.

———— and WEXLER, I. B.: Blood group paradoxes. *J.A.M.A.*, p. 1074, Dec. 15, 1956.

————: *Heredity of the Blood Groups.* New York, Grune & Stratton, 1958.

WILBER, C. G.: Physiological regulations and the origin of human types. *Human Biology, 29*:329-336, 1957.

WILDER, H. H.: *A Laboratory Manual of Anthropometry.* Philadelphia, Blakiston, 1920.

————: *The Pedigree of the Human Race.* New York, Holt, 1926.

WILSON, T. M.: On the presence of fluorine as a test for the fossilization of animal bones. *Amer. Naturalist, 29*:301-317, 439-456, 719-725, 1895.

WOO JU-KANG: Human fossils found in China and their significance in human evolution. *Scientia Sinica*, 5:289-297, 1956.

————: New materials of *Dryopithecus* from Keiyuan, Yunnan. *Vertebrata Palasiatica*, 2:38-42, 1958.

————: Tzeyang paleolithic man—earliest representative of modern man in China. *Am. J. Phys. Anthropol.*, n.s. 16:459-471, 1959.

———— and CHOW MIN-CHEN: New materials of the earliest primate known in China. *Vertebrata Palasiatica*, 1:267-272, 1957.

WOODWARD, A. S.: *The Earliest Englishman.* London, Watts & Co., 1948.

WOODWORTH, R. S.: *Heredity and Environment.* New York, Social Science Research Council, 1942.

WORMINGTON, H. M.: *Prehistoric Indians of the Southwest.* Colorado Museum of Natural History, Denver, 1947.

————: *Ancient Man in North America*, 4th ed. revised. Denver Museum of Natural History, 1957.

WRIGHT, S.: The roles of mutation, inbreeding, crossbreeding, and selection in evolution. *Proc. Sixth Int. Congress Genetics, 1*:356-366, 1932, Ithaca, New York.

WUNDERLY, J.: The Keilor fossil skull: anatomical description. *Mem. Nat. Museum,* Melbourne No. *13;* 57-69, 1943.

YERKES, R. M.: *Chimpanzees.* New Haven, Yale Univ. Press, 1943.

―――― and A. W.: *The Great Apes.* New Haven, Yale Univ. Press, 1934.

YULE, G. Y. and KENDALL, M. G.: *An Introduction to the Theory of Statistics,* 14th edition. London, Griffin & Co., 1950.

ZEUNER, F. E.: *Dating the Past,* 4th ed. New York, Longmans, 1957.

――――: Time rates of organic evolution. *Bull. Nat. Inst. Science of India,* No. 7, New Delhi, 1955, pp. 276-289.

ZUCKERMAN, S.: *The Social Life of Monkeys and Apes.* New York, Harcourt, 1932.

――――: *Functional Affinities of Man, Monkeys, and Apes.* New York, Harcourt, 1933.